RAISING
RICH KIDS

RAISING
RICH KIDS

Gerald Le Van

To order additional copies of this book, contact:
Xlibris Corporation
1-888-795-4274
www.Xlibris.com
Orders@Xlibris.com
18135

CONTENTS

INTRODUCTION

I help families resolve disputes about money. Some work together in the family business. Others are at odds about inheritance. My practice rests on a three-legged stool: *families, money and trouble.*

Money may be the last taboo topic for family discussion. Few talk productively about what money means, about what money can buy and what it cannot. Some deny that money conversations are necessary. Others assume that because they haven't talked, everyone understands and agrees—which they usually don't.

Like you, my clients worry that their children will mismanage money. Or worse that money will corrupt them. They want their children to develop healthy habits and attitudes about money but don't know quite where to begin or how to help. This story is about parents who face the same dilemma.

The setting is a summer camp reunion in October 2032. The main characters are a half dozen former campers now in their early forties. All are affluent, some wealthy. Quite innocently Betsy coaxes them to join a light-hearted discussion about "raising rich kids". Their frank and sometimes painful conversations expose a variety of turbulent unresolved issues about money. They leave the Camp Denim reunion with deeper insights into money's role in their family lives.

You will identify with them. I hope this story will jump start productive money conversations in your family.

Gerald Le Van
Black Mountain, North Carolina
February 2003

ACKNOWLEDGEMENTS

This book began with John L. Levy, former executive director of the Jungian Society of San Francisco. Over five years John patiently interviewed wealthy parents, their children and their respective therapists. He summarized these interviews and gave them to me to use as I saw fit.

The core of John's summary is reproduced here as "The Unpublished Writings of F. Willard FitzWillard". Wise, thoughtful and generous, John Levy is indeed the very antithesis of the scoundrel FitzWillard who plagiarized others' insights.

In 1986, after twenty-five years as a trust and estates lawyer and law professor, I entered family business consulting. In a variety of settings since, all of my client business families have been troubled about money or at least very uneasy about its hazards for their children. I have witnessed too many exceedingly sad situations that might have been averted by parents who better understood how to help their children develop healthy money habits and attitudes—situations that might have been averted by parents who better understood their *own* money hang-ups.

I'm greatly indebted to my friend and colleague Robert S. Cottor, M.D., a leading child psychiatrist, for professional insights and kind encouragement, to my sturdy study group Tom Hubler, John Messervey, Jeff Rothstein, Glenn Swogger, M.D., and Tom Zanecchia who favored me with a group edit, and to Beth Flowers, M.D., and my neighbor Carol Cauthen for their candid reactions and suggestions.

My editor, Margaret Marchuk, constant and fearless in the muzzle of an impatient creative ego did her usual superb job as did Nancy Walker, my assistant, who does more than I can imagine (or desire to know) to keep our ship on course.

Gerald Le Van

CHAPTER 1

Storm Shelter

Six children sat in a rough half circle near the entrance to the cave, their silhouettes backlit by intermittent lightning.

The teenage girl with wet hair and the boy with his arm around her had organized the impromptu hike. The others had just followed along. They found a trail into the woods, and then lost it in a frantic search for shelter from the storm.

A tall, sinewy, statuesque girl of fifteen sat watching and listening. Next to her a boy sobbed quietly. The others pretended not to notice.

Scratching with a stick in the gravel, a girl with dark straight hair and Asian eyes spoke:

"I wonder what our parents are doing."

She looked younger than twelve.

"Learning how to raise rich kids!"

sobbed the boy.

"They should learn how to find lost kids!"

lisped the smallest boy with a heavy Latino accent. He had led them into the cave.

A blinding bolt of lightning cracked just outside the entrance. All blinked and shuddered. The smallest boy leaped into the tall girl's lap. The others laughed.

Embarrassed, he looked up at her,

"My name is Pepe. What's your name?"

She smiled,

"My name is Tikka and I live in Africa. Where do you live, Pepe?"

"In a house with Mama, Papa and my big brothers."

He put a finger on her cheek,

"Your skin is brown."

"Yes, lots of Africans have brown skin."

Pepe pointed to the boy next to the girl with wet hair.

"Is he your boyfriend?"

"No, he is my brother. We're twins."

"I have two brothers. I wanted to go with them but they gave me this *linterna* . . . to come with you."

"*Linterna?*"

"Uh . . . flashlight."

CHAPTER 2

The High Priest of Healthy Wealth

At his zenith around the year 2025, M. Willard FitzWillard was the high priest of the Healthy Wealth Movement. His company, FitzWealth, was its shrine and its wealthy FitzClients the faithful. His best seller "Let Money Solve Your Problems" was in its twelfth printing and had been translated into thirty languages.

As a young stockbroker, FitzWillard watched wealthy persons struggle with competing advisors, each jealous of the other, each jockeying for favor, each angling to be "captain of the team." Such ceaseless competition was inefficient, frustrating and unnecessarily expensive. Wealthy clients wanted seamless one-stop full-service that didn't require clients to referee. And that's exactly what FitzWealth provided.

FitzWealth provided lawyers, accountants, actuaries, appraisers, investment and business advisors and career counselors; bought and sold stocks, bonds, insurance, real estate, art, antiques and collectibles and acted as investment bankers and business brokers.

FitzWealth retained the finest physicians, nurses, dentists, psychiatrists, dieticians, pharmacists, personal trainers, bodyguards and morticians, in world-wide liaison with the finest hospitals, clinics and spas.

FitzWealth provided butlers, nannies, personal shoppers, personal chefs, architects, decorators, contractors, travel agents, travel companions and connections to all sorts of important persons—from college admissions directors to foreign governments.

At one time, most FitzClients lived in homes located or built, financed, remodeled, furnished, decorated, insured and protected by FitzWealth. Their homes were staffed and supervised by FitzWealth staff, who coordinated social schedules, kept children, arranged travels and essentially did whatever FitzClients neglected, didn't have time for or didn't want to do themselves.

FitzClients enjoyed excellent health care. Fine restaurants had advance notice of dietary restrictions. Bartenders enforced drinking limits. Waiters secreted dessert trays. Fine hotels furnished personal trainers fully briefed on exercise programs. Prescribed pills and favorite potions appeared in the bathroom.

"Wealth listens to wealth" FitzWillard was fond of saying. His dictum permeated his remarkable sales force, all sons and daughters of FitzClients eager for respectable work among their peers. The FitzWealth organization carefully insulated its privileged sales force against unpleasantness, such as criticisms and complaints about the service. Unpleasantness was handled by ordinary mortals.

For a time, FitzWealth was the largest personal provider to the wealthy of the world. For a time, FitzWillard reigned unchallenged as the high priest of The Healthy Wealth Movement. Sadly, however, his reign was cut short by runaway ambition.

FitzWealth's success inspired tough competitors, each claiming to offer more elaborate services than the other. To meet the competition, Fitz expanded too fast, borrowed too hastily, promised too much. Eventually he was deposed by a syndicate of defectors from his elite sales force backed by their families' money and out to prove themselves, in league with a surly band of lawyers, accountants and financial advisors earlier displaced by FitzWealth and out for revenge.

The high priest of Healthy Wealth died broke and in obscurity, attended at the end by his faithful nephew.

CHAPTER 3

The Lottery Ticket

Betsy checked her makeup and straight black hair, faced the communications module and began speaking.

"Hey Tribe!

It's September 12, 2032

I can't believe it's only six weeks until our 30th Camp Denim reunion?!!

I'm dying to learn what's become of us since puberty, and am dieting furiously in anticipation!

Remember the shy little girl who kept the diary? That was me, and my diary has the real dirt on

*all of you! Just to tease, I'm attaching a page.
Read it and squirm!*

See you there!"

Betsy opened a faded denim-bound diary to a page dated August 2, 2002. The paper was spotted by rain or sweat or who knows what. The diary provoked a strange internal reunion with the twelve-year-old Betsy who had written down the day's events. Strange . . . as though the child diarist had been a separate person rather than an earlier version of her present self. Betsy felt a sudden and overwhelming tenderness and compassion for that shy curious child. Tears gathered as she reread, and then carefully rewrote her memories of that day.

August 2, 2002

Another Rainy Day at Camp Denim

It had rained for three days. A cloudburst was in progress, lightning and thunder.

The Tribe, a cluster of a dozen scuzzy girls and boys, aged eleven to fourteen, huddled sullenly in the Camp Denim dining hall. Their counselors had run dry of fun ideas for a wet day. They had played all the camp games, retold all the camp stories, sung all the verses to all the camp songs. The Tribe was bored and restless. Suddenly inspired, a counselor named John remembered the lottery ticket in his pocket. Waiving it high above his head he asked:

"Hey, Tribe! Do you know what this is?"

Most knew.

"So what would you do if I gave it to you, and you won ten million dollars in the lottery tomorrow?!"

Giggles and groans from the Tribe. John playfully offered the lottery ticket to one camper then another, then another, jerking it away at the last moment. Campers responded:

"I'd turn off the rain!"

"I'd buy Camp Denim and fire John!"

"And sell the dining hall to McDonalds!"

Laughter.

"I would let everyone come to Camp Denim for free!"

. . . said an edgy voice. A clap of thunder. A sudden hush . . . the children still, the counselors solemn. A taboo had been broken. Camp Denim took great pains to be diverse, classless, and inclusive. Each child brought the same basic items to camp, no more. No fancy electronics, no expensive sneakers, no designer outfits.

Campers and counselors wore camp-issued clothes, used camp-issued gear.

No money changed hands at Camp Denim. Each child had an account at the camp store, with the same beginning balance. When spent, there was no more credit, no cash accepted. Much of the routine work was done by campers. They served in the food lines, washed dishes, cleaned the cabins, helped maintain the grounds.

Denim, the worldwide fabric—leveler of all races and classes— symbolized this classless camp society. Shorts and caps, mattress covers and aprons, all were made of denim. There were denim napkins for special meals. Badges awarded for archery, swimming, horsemanship, hiking, etc. were embroidered on a denim background. Even the camp flag was made of denim.

Privileged parents, concerned about social isolation in elite private schools, sent their children to Camp Denim for an egalitarian summer experience. Wealthier parents paid two camp fees, one for their own child, and the other to sponsor a child who couldn't otherwise attend because of financial need. Parents were never told which child they sponsored. Most campers knew something about the sponsor fund. Others suspected, but it wasn't cool to talk about it. You didn't want to hurt a sponsored camper's feelings. That's why:

"I would let everyone come to Camp Denim for free!"

. . . provoked such an uneasy silence. Glances from other counselors said, "OK John, you thought up this lottery stuff—now you own it." Thinking fast, John persisted:

"OK, OK, Tribe . . . . Now what happens to people who win the lottery?"

More camper responses:

"They buy mansions!"

"They buy jets!"

"They own football teams!"

"Their own Rap groups!"

"And party with the players!"

And after a moment . . .

"Their 'friends' take their money—like Pinocchio!"

Laughter.

"They get body guards."

"Their children get kidnapped!"

"They get divorced!"

"They go crazy!"

"They go broke!"

And from the smallest voice:

"They'd wish they hadn't won after all!"

Betsy attached the revised diary page to the videomail and pressed Send.

CHAPTER 4

Camp Denim 2032

Now that he owned Camp Denim everyone called him "Skipper" and he liked it.

John "Skipper" Shaw laughed aloud as he read Betsy's diary page. He vividly remembered that rainy day. Clowning with the lottery ticket almost cost him his job. He remembered point by point the blistering reprimand administered by the camp director:

- Counselors personify Camp Denim values at all times in all situations.

- Camp Denim values don't encourage gambling in any form, even if lotteries were legal in this state. They weren't at the time.

- Because family financial situations vary widely, some campers have things at home that other campers don't, and some campers can do things that other campers can't.

Tom Jenkins
917 597-0202

ual access to *everything* Camp

d campers hurts feelings and is

ary from a cynical world that
getting and spending. At Camp
rs, not consumers.

ttitudes towards money and
and fourteen. Camp Denim
ttitudes. "Hit the jackpot"
lotteries—aren't healthy.

... oκipper) Shaw swallowed this bitter medicine silently. "We learn by screwing up," he muttered.

Skipper Shaw had wanted to play professional baseball but couldn't hit a curve ball consistently. He was a stockbroker for a time but felt miscast. Then he worked in the family business until his father sold it. With his share of the sales proceeds, he made a down payment on Camp Denim, thereby acquiring a host of expensive problems. The prior owner had skimped on costly maintenance. Property taxes soared. Skipper underestimated the time and money required for recruiting. Most old campers returned, but too many new candidates went elsewhere. His advisors urged Skipper to sell.

Deep into negotiations with Disney Camps Worldwide, Skipper was contacted by representatives of an undisclosed Benefactor. The Benefactor proposed to lower and lengthen the payments on Skipper's camp loans. On land leased from Camp Denim, the Benefactor would construct a conference center (off-limits to campers) providing meeting facilities, guest sleeping rooms, space for Camp Denim's administrative offices, and a luxury penthouse for the Benefactor. Skipper would manage the conference center for five years in return for a generous salary and perks guaranteed by the Benefactor. To Hell with Disney, Skipper couldn't refuse.

Through the picture window in his office, Skipper Shaw gazed across Lake Denim towards the ranges of mountains coloring with fall foliage. He felt truly human here, always had, and always would. Forever a camper perhaps, but who cares? At age fifty-three he was living out his dream. Pinned to the opposite wall was a list of registrants and suggested discussion topics for the 30th reunion. On it he wrote: "Betsy's Workshop—"*Raising Rich Kids*".

CHAPTER 5

Replies

One hundred seventy-two boys and girls attended Camp Denim during the summer of 2002. Eleven were known dead. Only forty would return for their 30th Reunion.

What of the others who weren't coming? Who had a schedule conflict? Who didn't care? Who had dropped from sight? Who couldn't afford to come, or would be too embarrassed by fate or circumstances to show up? Who might be institutionalized, or in jail, or . . . ? So much can happen in thirty years.

Responses to Betsy's videomail arrived over several weeks. The first was an automated reply from the family of a camper she didn't remember. The attached obituary concluded: "The family suggests memorial gifts be made to Help for the Homeless."

————————

Reply from Sallie:

No picture, no pleasantries, Sallie demanded a private corner room
with bath overlooking the lake. Would there be accommodations
for her teenage twins if they chose to come? Would she be charged
for their meals? Betsy frowned and forwarded this one to Skipper.
Spoiled grownups were his department.

————————

Reply from Connie:

"Here's ol' Connie in her rollin' jail!"

. . . her famous face crinkling into a playful smile. The video
picture jiggled slightly from the motion of the private bus.
Country music in the background covered the soft engine roar.

"I'm somewhere in South America singin' to the troops."

A hand appeared with mascara.

"Them Chinese soldiers sure holler and clap. Nothin' like a little
music from down home."

The hand reappeared holding a makeup brush. Connie glowered,

"Buzz off, Lester, can't you see I'm talkin' to Betsy in cyberspace!"

The hand withdrew quickly.

"Your Chinese cousins said tell you hello. Can't get 'em to eat
grits though—slides right off their chopsticks. Tell Skipper to
hold me a parking space,"

. . . chuckled Connie, signing off with a wink not intended for Betsy.

Reply from Ernesto:

"Hi, China Doll."

Ernesto's handsome Latin face and familiar greeting stirred a secret crush Betsy had carried since their first summer at Camp Denim.

"You won't believe what's happening here in Columbia! The United Nations took a huge gamble sending in a Chinese peacekeeping force but it's paying off so far.

"They are really effective! First the Chinese crushed the drug lords' private armies. They arrested the drug lords and their lieutenants, charged them with 'crimes against humanity', and shipped them all to China for trial! They've burned the coca fields and blown up the labs where the locals made cocaine.

"The Columbians are offering incredible business opportunities to a select group of Chinese entrepreneurs—your family among them. Your brothers sold one of their Bogotá companies to me and promised to help me with the Chinese, if I'll help the Chinese with the Columbians.

"People here in Bogotá are safe for the first time in their lives. It's a new day.

"Betsy, you'll never guess who's entertaining the Chinese troops! None other than our own Connie Alden. Tell you all about it at Camp Denim. Bringing my boys to meet you.

"Bye, China Doll."

Reply from Roger:

. . . wearing an elegant three-piece suit, seated in a burgundy leather chair, holding a very expensive fountain pen. Roger's voice was stentorian.

"Hi, Betsy! Loved your videomail. I tried to buy that lottery ticket from Skipper John, you know. He wouldn't sell—said he was in lots of trouble because of it.

"Saw 'Healthy Wealth' listed as your dissertation topic on the Internet. Did you know that M. Willard FitzWillard was my uncle? He wasn't the huckster the media liked to portray. The hucksters were those cynical senior executive goons he couldn't control. They're the ones who tried to wet nurse all the wealthy of the world. They didn't care a flip about their clients' welfare or about Healthy Wealth. They just wanted money, and they made oceans of it for a while. Finally got what they deserved.

"Uncle Fitz deserved more. He was a serious thinker you know. He wanted people to master money—not the other way around. I think he was relieved when FitzWealth folded. The goons gave his book that corny title "Let Money Solve Your Problems" I'm sure you've read it carefully. 'Healthy Wealth' is quite a sophisticated concept.

"I spent lots of time with Uncle Fitz during his last years. I'm his executor, you know. One of my responsibilities is assembling his unpublished writings. They're quite extensive. Want to see them sometime?

"Watch your purse 'till I see you at Camp Denim."

"BINGO!" Betsy shouted.

Last Reply:

Betsy whooped as she clicked open the last videomail reply. There were Doctors Fred DeWitt and Avery Parsons, white coats and stethoscopes, standing in front of a jungle hut squinting in the midday sun.

Betsy barely remembered Avery, the only member of The Tribe quieter than she, shyer than she, more serious than she. Other campers mocked and teased Fred, but Avery had befriended him.

Fred spoke first.

> "Greetings from two worn out docs at Camp Desperate in scenic Africa. I'm just passing through, but Avery hangs out here a lot. Fun activities like malnutrition, malaria, and long lines . . . all emergencies. The AIDS festival is year-round. Their favorite sport is making war, not love. Lake Putrid is a great place to swim after work if your nose doesn't work. The Reunion sounds like a great nap. I can hardly wait!"

Avery listened to Fred, amused and serene, and then spoke.

> "Small world indeed. Fred's learning fast. He's really good with children. Everyone's overwhelmed at first." Cupping a hand over her mouth and pretending to whisper out of Fred's earshot, "I don't think he's wet the bed yet!"

Just then a frightfully emaciated child, apparently disoriented, wandered stiffly into the picture and clung to Avery's leg looking up at her with sunken eyes. Fred turned away. Stroking the child, Avery said calmly,

> "We'll see you at Camp Denim, Betsy. Got to go now."

Betsy burst into tears, sobbing and shaking. The cool analytical PhD candidate, the patient researcher of the hazards of wealth, was completely undone by the picture of this pathetic child. Her own healthy children had everything, wanted for nothing. Betsy, the pampered and protected daughter of privilege felt raw shame.

CHAPTER 6

Gilded Angst

2002:

T welve year-old Betsy listened carefully, writing in her diary, saying nothing. Her own father traveled with a bodyguard, overseas with several bodyguards. During her childhood the family lived in a very large house protected by alarm systems, electric fences, and armed men stationed at the locked gate. Her parents brought her to Camp Denim on the company jet, their goodbyes interspersed with warnings about her personal safety. Confinement inside the gates of Camp Denim meant liberation for Betsy.

2032:

Next to her Camp Denim diary lay Betsy's draft proposal for her doctoral dissertation titled "Gilded Angst: Children and the Healthy Wealth Movement Successes and Failures." In the preface Betsy wrote:

The greatest transfer of private wealth in human history is well underway.

Never have so many become so wealthy. Never have the wealthy left so much wealth behind. As the wealthy die, trillions flow from their estates to favored charities and fortunate heirs.

"Trillionheirs" as the media call them, luxuriate in a new gilded age underwritten by inheritances. Conspicuous consumption rages once again. Opulence and ostentation abound. The chasm between rich and poor grows wider.

Never before has there been such widespread anxiety about the potential harm inheritance can do. Wealthy parents agonize:

> *How much should I give my children?*
> *How much should I withhold?*
> *How much should I control what I give them?*
> *How much should my children struggle?*

Medieval alchemists failed to turn lead into gold. Wealthy twenty-first century parents fear a reverse alchemy. Will their trillionheirs transmute inherited gold into leaden lives—hollow, shallow, self-absorbed, addicted, indolent, meaningless, wasted?

The potentially corrupting influence of unearned wealth is not a new or novel concern. However, The Healthy Wealth Movement introduced new and novel prescriptions for wealthy parents' gilded angst. Healthy Wealth advocates insisted that the corrupting influence of money can be minimized by enlightened giving, withholding, or controlling. To parents already preoccupied with money, a money solution to a money problem seemed sensible—like fighting fire with fire.

Through personal interviews with a selected group of 'trillionheirs' whose parents have followed the advice of various Healthy Wealth advocates, I propose to test the efficacy of their counsel.

As the daughter of a very wealthy Chinese-American family, Betsy was herself a trillionheiress. She understood how wealth listens to wealth—why wealthy persons tend to put greater trust in other wealthy persons.

Her soft and understated interview style was beguiling. Petite and guardedly intense, she still came across as the "China Doll" Ernesto had dubbed her during Camp Denim days. Wealthy persons trusted her, confided in her, and opened up to her. Betsy was an able teacher, coach, and leader. Research assistants would learn much from her.

Now with free access to FitzWillard's unpublished writings, the Camp Denim reunion would crown Betsy's research.

CHAPTER 7

Ernesto

2002:

*E*rnesto, also twelve years old, stole a quick look at Betsy during the tension that followed "... free for everyone!" Ernesto's mother was the cook for Betsy's family in the big house. Betsy and Ernesto had never spoken until this, their very first camp experience. Quiet, athletic, popular with his schoolmates, Ernesto hadn't dreamed of summer camp until one of his coaches suggested Camp Denim. The sponsor fund paid his expenses. Neither Betsy's parents nor Ernesto's mother knew the other's child would be at Camp Denim until they met at the gate.

2032:

Seated next to a window in business class high over the South Atlantic, Ernesto replayed Betsy's videomail admiring her pretty

Asian face. He didn't remember the rainy day or the lottery ticket. But their parents' awkward meeting on the first day of camp had changed his life.

Betsy's father belonged to an influential Chinese trading family. Impressed by Ernesto's intelligence and presence, the family had subsidized his business education. Over time the family taught Ernesto as much about their companies as an outsider was permitted to know.

Leveraging his American upbringing, his Latin heritage, flawless Spanish, and uncanny business and diplomatic instincts, Ernesto became the trading company's chief representative in Central and South America. Ernesto mentored Betsy's younger brothers, pushed them into the spotlight and stayed in the background. The family trusted him as much as they could trust someone not their own. But he was not a member of the inner circle. He pretended not to understand Chinese.

Ernesto bought the family's Columbian export company and was on his way to Bogotá to take charge. His wife and three sons would remain in Havana for the time being. He missed them terribly.

CHAPTER 8

Sallie

2002:

Sallie had meant to sound nasty when she blurted:

> *"I would let everyone come to*
> *Camp Denim for free!"*

Sallie didn't want to be there. All her friends from private school went to an exclusive camp with no sponsor fund. Her mother told her all about the sponsor fund, assuring Sallie she would be able to "spot" the sponsored campers.

Though her parents didn't tell her until much later, Sallie herself was sponsored. They were heavily in debt for Sallie's private school tuition. When it was The Tribe's turn to wash dishes for a week, Sallie refused. She offered to pay Ernesto to take her place on the cleaning crew. Overhearing, Betsy did Sallie's work, leaving her a note "from a secret friend". Sallie couldn't have paid Ernesto anyway. Her camp store account was depleted after the first week.

2032:

Sallie ignored Betsy's videomail for several days. She still detested Camp Denim and had long ago lost contact with everyone she had known there. She had nothing in common with those silly egalitarians.

Skin deep, Sallie was quite attractive, some would say a beauty. Her long raven hair and splendid figure turned heads routinely. Her pretty face was not a poker face. Irritation or discontent displayed on her brow, jaws and eyes in unflattering ways; her voice became sharp and whining. Unskilled at putting unpleasantness behind her, Sallie's face and voice expressed accumulated discontents. Fortunately for those around her, she was equally inept at concealing amusement, approval, or pleasure.

The only child of middle aged parents, Sallie managed to marry three rich men. Two divorce settlements made her rich in her own right. Her third marriage was solid enough. Generous trusts created by her second husband guaranteed lifetime support for their twins, Sallie's only children. The twins' trusts were laced with financial incentives and disincentives advocated by The Healthy Wealth Movement. If giving or withholding trust funds could foster good behavior and discourage the bad, Sallie's children would become model citizens.

Ironically, her twins seemed totally indifferent to money. A friendly sibling rivalry revolved around who could live on less. Neither drove a car nor wanted one. Their used clothes came from charity shops. Neither used drugs; neither had problems in school. Their friends—all children of wealthy families—shared the same minimalist lifestyle. The more Sallie encouraged them to spend, the thriftier they became, routinely refusing Sallie's gifts. Their stepfather was quietly amused.

When Sallie got around to Betsy's videomail and read the diary page, she was furious! She well remembered that rainy day and exactly what she had said! She would go to the damned Camp Denim reunion and set things straight!

CHAPTER 9

Roger

2002:

Roger shuddered when he saw the lottery ticket. While at Camp Denim, Roger escaped the chaos at home, his parents' shouting, the harassing telephone calls from bill collectors he sometimes answered after school.

At Camp Denim Roger escaped never knowing if there would be money for school lunches, allowance, clothes. It wasn't that his father gambled. He didn't. It was his mother. She was always shopping, always buying, always spending. She drank when there was no more credit. With a growing lump in his throat, it was Roger who shouted that the lottery winner:

" . . . would go crazy!

. . . would go broke!"

2032:

Careful, thoughtful, correct, incessantly quantifying, tough enough, Roger Ringgold was Cyberbank's youngest ever Chairman and CEO. A cyberbanker's cyberbanker, money fascinated Roger, excited him.

Roger was a close observer of what people did for money, did with money, and what money did to them. According to Roger, of all the influences on human behavior money was the most powerful, the most tangible and the most measurable.

Beginning in the 1990s there had been an explosion in personal wealth in the United States. Twice in the twenty-first century Congress had repealed all wealth transfer taxes—the estate tax and gift tax—only to reinstate them hurriedly, each time with fewer loopholes. Wealth transfer taxes accounted for an increasing proportion of federal revenue.

Sophisticated tax vehicles enabled wealthy persons to move large amounts of wealth to children and grandchildren at little tax cost on the transfer. Yet parents seemed to use these vehicles less and less. Internal Revenue Service statistics confirmed that charities were getting more from wealthy parents while their children and grandchildren were getting less.

Roger pondered these trends. If money is the chief influence on human behavior, then how can money be given, withheld, or controlled to encourage good behavior and discourage destructive behavior? If money can't buy love or respect, can money nevertheless keep children's attention, or protect them from greedy spouses, or teach sound values to grandchildren?

How can money (or the lack thereof) encourage education, the work ethic, good deeds and philanthropy for the "right" causes? How can money discourage indulgence, indolence, addiction and other self-destructive behaviors?

No one was more taken with The Healthy Wealth Movement than Roger Ringgold. After all, he had been the late M. Willard FitzWillard's favorite nephew.

CHAPTER 10

Connie

2002:

Connie couldn't wait to return to Camp Denim each year. She thought and talked about camp all year long. At Camp Denim she could be an unrestrained tomboy for four whole weeks—ride horses, play softball, dunk the boys in the lake, play pranks on the counselors. Once Connie was caught trying to flush the nurse's kitten down a toilet. Once she jumped from the moving camp bus on a dare. It was Connie who shouted that the lottery winner:

". . . could buy a football team!

. . . could buy a Rap group!"

Then she groined the boy next to her, who doubled over with pain and laughter. "Hormones in tennis shoes," said Connie's father. By age thirteen, Connie had already smoked a joint, had already let a boy touch her breasts. Some would say Connie was just a free spirit;

others would say a pain in the ass. She wrote bawdy camp songs and sang them beautifully.

2032:

Incredibly funny, outrageously outspoken, Connie Alden was the most successful country singer of her decade. Audiences cheered and sobbed as Connie closed concerts with her signature song, "Big Little Brother". Connie entertained international peacekeeping forces wherever they were sent. After her brother died, she spent a year giving benefit performances for research on cystic fibrosis.

Though Connie was a star and lived a star's life floated on oceans of money, the tabloids seldom penetrated her privacy. According to the gossip columns she had few friends, no husband, no children, and spent most of the time traveling on her private bus. Any known outrageous behavior took place in full view of her audiences. Who would dare miss the Camp Denim reunion if Connie Alden were coming!

CHAPTER 11

Fred

2002:

It was Fred who had said:

"They'd wish they hadn't won after all!"

Fred was the smallest of the eleven-year-olds at Camp Denim. Fred hadn't wanted to go. He was terribly homesick, but not for the home awaiting him after camp. He longed for the home he had before his parents' divorce, before his mother had married the doctor, before Fred had to share a bedroom with a detestable fourteen year-old stepbrother who teased and bullied him.

Fred's stepfather was always at the hospital, always "making rounds", always answering his beeper, always exhausted, always cross with Fred. Fred's mother promised that his new doctor Dad would give them things his real father never could—including four weeks at Camp Denim.

But Fred would give it all back just to live again with Mom and his real Dad. At camp sometimes Fred cried out in the night. Sometimes he wet the bed.

2032:

Exhausted, Frederick DeWitt, M.D., fell fully-clothed into bed. Two weeks gone and two weeks yet to go on his first assignment with Physicians Without Borders. Fred had prepared himself for Mexico or perhaps Haiti, but never dreamed he would be sent to this primitive field hospital in Africa.

Never had Fred witnessed such need, such poverty, such suffering, such limited medical facilities, so many serious diseases. He saw desperate patients sixteen hours a day.

Fred wasn't sure why he became a physician. The responsibility was enormous, the risks huge, the hours grueling, the earnings less than lawyers. As an eighteen-year-old college freshman, Fred disappeared into medicine's black hole that thereafter consumed virtually all of his time and energy. He was always harried, always tired, getting grumpy like the stepfather he had grown to admire. His cozy suburban practice was spoiled by impossible patients, impossible colleagues, and an impossible medical bureaucracy.

Small world. Chief of staff at the field hospital was The Reverend Avery Parsons, M.D., whom Fred had known at Camp Denim. Avery, her parents and her husband, all physicians, lived, worked, and raised their children in Africa. Avery and Fred watched Betsy's videomail together. Both would attend the reunion.

CHAPTER 12

Avery

2002:

Avery came to Camp Denim by accident. She was destined for a church camp, but lightning struck its chapel and the ensuing fire destroyed half the dormitories. To Avery, Camp Denim was anything but rustic—it was sheer luxury compared to the mission station that was home for her in Africa. Camp Denim's careful egalitarianism was lost on Avery. To her every camper seemed rich. Though there were other African-American campers, it took time to adjust to so many white children. She remembered the incident about the lottery ticket—she had not heard of lotteries before.

2032:

Over the past five decades, millions of Africans had died of AIDS. Her physician father and physician mother had gone to Africa in the 1990s, during the worst part of the dreadful AIDS epidemic.

An effective AIDS vaccine had been developed at the Bill and Melinda Gates Foundation, but vaccination had not become generally available in Africa until a few years before. Still more millions were HIV positive, treatable if not curable. Avery and her physician husband worked in a Gates Foundation field hospital.

Access to the AIDS vaccination and treatment was largely controlled by Africa's military dictators. Foreign medical personnel were relatively safe, though unwitting pawns in the dictators' struggles for power and territorial control. Avery and her husband were sustained by a continuing assurance they had been called of God.

Their children had been born in Africa. Tikka, their oldest daughter would accompany Avery to the Camp Denim Reunion.

CHAPTER 13

Gathering

As Skipper Shaw hoisted the Camp Denim flag into a late October breeze, it billowed like a long full skirt turning slowly. Skipper smiled.

All seemed ready for the reunion. The campgrounds were immaculate. The maintenance crew worked weekends through September to patch and paint the worst of wear and tear left behind by three hundred hyperactive summer campers. By tradition, juvenile graffiti inside the rustic cabins was left intact to be rediscovered during future reunions.

An advance videomail contained room assignments, a schedule of meals and events, and a request to wear denim jeans during the week-end. Special denim shirts would be provided at registration. Each reunion returnee was assigned to "an adventure group for fun learning and exciting discussion." Betsy would lead a group discussion about raising rich kids. The sponsor fund was available to subsidize reunion travel if needed . . . but no one applied.

The lobby of the Camp Denim Conference Center was alive with returning campers—shrieks and laughter, hugs and smiling once-over glances. Reproduced on the back of each returnee's denim shirt was a larger than life-sized color photograph of him or her taken at camp thirty years ago.

Ernesto's three boys chased each other chattering in Spanish, teasing with Fred and his partner. Sallie sat in a corner, her denim shirt and elegant designer jeans complemented by a huge sapphire dinner ring, diamond-bordered. Sallies twins wore threadbare chic. Roger, a cashmere blue blazer over his denim, talked earnestly with Betsy who was taking notes, a delicate dragonfly clasp holding her hair.

As Avery was registering, Connie clomped through the outside door in gaudy red cowboy boots and denim mini-skirt, "Oops, am I in the wrong goddamned nursing home *again*?!!" The fun was underway!

After luncheon introductions and lusty camp songs, Skipper led a tour of the Camp Denim grounds. Oaks, maples, dogwoods, and poplars were nearing peak fall colors—yellow, orange, copper and red leaves overhead and underfoot.

Too bad, Skipper said, that campers miss the fall foliage and the spring wild flowers. Too bad they come in summer when haze obscures long views of the mountains and balmy days turn warm, but infinitely more humane than summer days and nights in Miami, Atlanta, St. Louis or Phoenix.

During the spirited inter-tribal softball game Ernesto hit a home run into the woods behind center field. His three boys raced around the bases. At an evening campfire following a barbecue, Avery wept with others as a sober and serious Connie sang "Big Little Brother" into the night. Threatening clouds were covering the moon and stars.

An impromptu cash bar tried unsuccessfully to close at midnight. An hour later, her journal entries done, Betsy turned out the light and fell asleep to a rainy night at Camp Denim. All slept save Skipper and one other.

CHAPTER 14

Money Talks

Kitchen clatter and smells of bacon and coffee greeted Betsy as she tacked a poster on the bulletin board outside her assigned meeting place, the Pow Wow Room.

"Raising Rich Kids"

it said,

"Ernesto, Sallie, Connie, Fred, Roger,
Avery and Betsy"

The weeks just prior to the reunion had been a blur of excitement and exhaustion. Betsy devoured the unpublished (and heretofore unknown) writings of M. Willard FitzWillard, marveling at the stark disparity between the private man and his public image. The media portrayed FitzWillard as a charlatan snake oil salesman to the rich. His private writings revealed a thoughtful and sensitive student of the money dilemma.

The Pow Wow Room held a rustic oak table and eight very comfortable executive chairs. A floor-to-ceiling screen and elegant sound system actuated by state-of-the-art audio-visual equipment displayed old camp photos and sound bites of camp songs interspersed with a montage of clever television commercials showing affluent children and teenagers having a good time on carousels, cruise ships, and convertibles. The familiar face of H. Willard FitzWillard appeared from time to time, as though blessing the revelry.

"Is this *Raising Wretched Kids*?!!"

Connie burst through the door, hugged Betsy and sprawled in a chair hanging a red booted leg over the arm. Fred and Avery sat quietly together talking of things medical and missionary in low friendly tones. Connie rolled her eyes in their direction then towards Betsy.

Roger the cyberbanker took the seat next to Connie who immediately assaulted him with conversation, her face uncomfortably close to his. Handsome Ernesto flashed a smile and seated himself next to Betsy who felt his magnetic field. Sallie arrived last, sulking and sitting alone.

Betsy began:

"It's just too ironic that Roger's uncle was none other than H. Willard FitzWillard. I didn't know that until Roger answered my videomail about this very meeting. As you know I'm writing my PhD dissertation about the impact of FitzWillard's 'Healthy Wealth Movement' on our children. Roger is letting me read Fitz's unpublished writings. It's like striking gold!"

"Perhaps a good place to begin is with that rainy day here at Camp Denim thirty years ago when John—uh, Skipper—taunted us with the lottery ticket. Does anyone but me remember?"

"I do," smiled Avery. "I had to ask what a lottery ticket was. Could have been a condom for all I knew then. I was a refugee from a church camp."

"I remember it rained for a long time, and that Connie groined me," mused Ernesto. "I remember meeting Betsy's parents at the gate. Were they surprised to see me! My Mom was their cook. They didn't know I was coming to camp. I was on scholarship."

"How did you feel about that, Ernesto?" asked Betsy.

"I wasn't ashamed at all," Ernesto replied. "Mom prepared me. She said I belonged at Camp Denim as much as you did. She was proud I had a scholarship. She said I deserved to go. She said your parents just bought your way in."

The others tensed at Ernesto's bluntness. Betsy eased them.

"Ernesto has worked for my father for years. He's just bought one of Dad's companies. Anyone else remember?"

"Damn right!" blurted Sallie. "I was miserable in this wretched place! *My parents couldn't even afford Camp Denim!* They wouldn't tell me they ran out of money paying my private school tuition! I was humiliated when I found out!"

Sallie began to sob.

"Let's take a break," said Betsy.

CHAPTER 15

Round Two

Betsy found her in the ladies room.

"Look Sallie, I'm really sorry about this. I had no idea . . ."

Sallie was working on her composure,

"Don't stop for me," she insisted.

Betsy flirted with halting the discussion but dismissed the idea. She shouldn't expect the others to carry Sallie's baggage. As they left the ladies room Fred appeared offering Sallie a cup of coffee.

"Round Two," announced Betsy.

Sallie was the first to return to the table where she sat very still staring into her coffee. The others took their seats quietly.

"Enough camp memories for now," said Betsy as she reached for the video controls.

"Wait, Betsy."

It was Fred.

> "I've got something to unload. I was the one who said the lottery winner would regret it. My Mom and Dad had an ugly divorce. My Mom had just married a physician and moved us in with his family. I was miserable here. If I could have anything money could buy, I didn't want it."

Under the table Sallie reached for Fred's hand intending to squeeze it. But Fred was leaning back in his chair, eyes closed. Betsy fingered the video control.

> "One more interruption."

This time it was Roger the cyberbanker.

"Going to fill us in on Uncle Fitz, Roger?"

> "Later, Betsy."

Roger heaved a huge sigh then talked haltingly, painfully, sometimes stammering.

> "I . . . I was the kid who said the lottery winner would go crazy, go broke . . . My mother was a compulsive spender . . . . Our household was chaos . . . . I grew up associating money with craziness. Camp Denim was the eye of the

hurricane—four weeks of sanity! I hated to go home."

"Uncle Fitz was my mother's brother. He knew about her spending. I'm sure he bailed us out from time to time. Somehow I had to make sense out of money . . . Perhaps that's why I'm a banker. I needed to control the monster that wrecked my household . . . I've said more than I meant to say . . . Please keep it in this room."

All nodded. Roger turned to look out the window, eyes wide, lump in throat. For the moment he was the troubled boy on that rainy day at Camp Denim.

"Oh how I wish I had a money hang-up so I could join this exclooooosive club."

It was Connie.

"Singin' jus' turns into money! Whoohee! I love the stuff—could jus' wallow in it. Not a very good shopper, though. Some things I haven't learned how to buy."

The others leaned forward with "haven't learned to buy what?" looks. Connie blew them a kiss then gave them the finger.

"Well," sighed Betsy, "there goes my lesson plan."

"I was going to show videos of FitzWillard with sound bites of his sayings. But let's try something else. I found some passages in Fitz's unpublished papers that would be fun to discuss. Here's a printed copy for each of you. Suppose we pair up after lunch. Talk with your partner about these passages and report back to the group this afternoon. OK?"

"If you'll let me pick the partners, I'll put Avery with Ernesto, Connie with Roger, and Sallie with Fred."

Each took a copy and left the room.

"Whew!" thought Betsy. "What a miscalculation! That lottery ticket turned fun into serious fast. Maybe they'll lighten up after lunch."

She read again the slip she had given them.

> *Why Struggle?* The U.S. Army once challenged recruits to "Be All You Can Be!" You trillionheirs will never need to struggle in order to survive. You will never be driven by life's necessities. You will never know what you might have accomplished with your back to the wall, without the family safety net. No one has devised a substitute for struggle, its lessons and benefits.
>
> Can we become our best selves without struggle? Not having to struggle makes it hard for you to stick to your goals in the face of setbacks and frustrations. Too often your goals are ill-defined, particularly your career goals. Too often your motivation is short-lived and lacks intensity. Self-discipline requires focused and sustained energy. Self-discipline requires you to postpone gratification for ultimately higher rewards. You need self-discipline not only for work but for significant human relationships. Lack of self-discipline is a major life-long cause of difficulty.
>
> *Too Many Choices?* Excessive options plague the wealthy. You have too many choices. Few

inheritors cope successfully with all the options money can buy. Too many options can paralyze decision-making.

Gilt Guilty. Guilt is rampant among the trillionheirs. It's hard to accept unmerited good fortune. You may be consciously apologetic or arrogantly contemptuous—both are ways of coping with your unrecognized guilt feelings. The rich who didn't earn it crave a sense of entitlement that forever eludes them.

CHAPTER 16

Lunch Time

Reunion lunches at Camp Denim followed a ritual pattern.

Tribes sat together, sang camp songs, poked fun, reminisced, and tried to look attentive as Skipper John effused the essential messages:

"Welcome back.

"We remember you and have missed you.

"Take time to relive the fun you had here.

"Enjoy the beautiful surroundings and our new facilities.

"Send us your children as campers.

"Recruit your children's friends whose parents can afford us.

"Be alert for promising scholarship campers.

"Donate big money for scholarships and new facilities.

"Above all revere Skipper John for his wisdom and leadership."

At least nature was cooperating with Betsy's workshop. Overnight rain had become intermittent mountain thundershowers that canceled outdoor activities after lunch. Betsy's partners sought dry places to do their homework. Avery and Ernesto chose a corner of the lobby. Connie and Roger a picnic pavilion open on four sides. Fred and Sallie returned to the Pow Wow Room.

At college reunions, even at high school reunions, the faces and voices of your classmates haven't changed that much even if the intervening years have grossly rearranged their hair and bodies. The memories you resurrect together have at least some dim connection with the current adult world.

It's a stretch to reconnect with pubescent friends from summer camp's four-week dream world. It's more challenging to find common adult ground with others we knew only as children.

Reconnecting wasn't awkward for Avery and Ernesto. Both lived global lives closely connected to the developing world. Their children were growing up among other languages, learning to deal with other cultures. Both had brought children to the reunion. More than likely they were playing together.

CHAPTER 17

Take A Hike

Though they had never been to a summer camp—and flatly refused to go—Sallie's twins Katelyn and Brad were eager to explore the mountains surrounding Camp Denim, rain notwithstanding. During a brief break in the weather the twins organized a hike. Having been abandoned by his older brothers, Ernesto's youngest boy, Pepe, pleaded to go with them. With some misgivings Ernesto consented.

> "Stick to the trails and come back quick if it begins to rain," he warned. "Be back by supper—take water and hats." The twins agreed.

Tikka made friends with Betsy's daughter Ming, who convinced Fitz Ringgold to join them and the twins.

Ten minutes into the woods the rain resumed. At first the hikers joked and bantered. Thunder rumbled closer. Lightning flashed and crackled. In heavy rain they wandered off the trail. Air temperature dropped sharply and winds increased as hail began to pelt them. There were no more jokes. They were lost. The ground was covered with hailstones.

The children sought shelter under a granite outcrop that offered only slight protection. Trees danced wildly. Lightning was almost constant.

Sitting on the ground, Pepe spotted an opening in the rocks below the outcrop and wriggled in. The others followed.

CHAPTER 18

Connie and Roger

"*Dear God I love this place!*" shouted Connie as she settled down across from Roger at a table inside the screened picnic pavilion.

Even at close range they would have to talk loudly above the rumble of heavy rain. Roger knew he needed to relax but Connie wasn't exactly relaxing company. He wasn't accustomed to the society of a rich and famous country singer with a loud and sometimes lascivious mouth. He folded his expensive raincoat and pulled a slip of paper from his shirt pocket. "Betsy insists," he said weakly.

"Don't read to me yet, Roger. Let's talk first. I'm not sure I even remember you."

"OK, Connie. Who is 'Big Little Brother' in that song you sing?"

Gone was the animation from Connie's face. She swallowed.

"I had an older brother with cystic fibrosis. He needed lots of care and treatment that wasn't covered by Daddy's health insurance. I was his nurse lots of the time when Mama was at work. I called him "big little brother" to cheer him up. I was going to be a pediatric nurse some day. Then he died. My nursing's in the song I guess. Not many people know about this, Roger. It's not in my press kit. You won't give me away will you?"

"Of course not, Connie.

"Children of your own?"

"No, no husband, no children. Just a damned old bus, a producer, a make-up man, and a travel schedule. Never had the time for homebound arrangements. Always moving. Glamorous, isn't it?"

"No boyfriends?"

"Out-of-bounds, Cyber Scrooge.

"What does it say on the paper, Roger?"

Roger produced an elegant pair of reading glasses, cleared his throat, and read aloud his uncle's ruminations. Connie rambled on as though she hadn't heard.

"I live in bubble wrap most of the time. Protect my voice from heat and cold. Protect my privacy from goon reporters. Protect my sanity from adoring fans that suck the life out of you if you let them near you."

"Is it a struggle?"

"Damn right I struggle, Roger. I struggle every time I face an audience that adores me but wants to be there if I screw up. I struggle every time I sing 'Big Little Brother.' I struggle when I look out my bus window at a school yard at recess time. I struggle when big time entertainers invite me to their cocaine parties, and I so want to get out of my lonely head I can't stand it."

"But you *made* it, Connie. You aren't some spoiled trillionheir."

"I inherited a *voice*. I didn't *earn* it. It just turns into money."

A change of wind direction blew rain through the screen. They moved to another table.

"Roger, are you rich?"

"I guess so, Connie, but not as rich as you."

"Who's 'rich', Roger?"

"Uncle Fitz said you're rich if you can continue a high lifestyle indefinitely, without working and with low risk."

"Does being rich make you uncomfortable, Roger?"

"Yes."

"Why?"

"I didn't earn it. I wanted to be a banker so Uncle Fitz opened all the right doors.

"Uncle Fitz made me rich as surely as if he had given me the money.

"I worked for it of course. But success was a sure thing with Uncle Fitz behind me."

"So you never struggled?"

"Not really. Never had my back to the wall."

"And when your Uncle Fitz started to lose it?"

"His creditors couldn't touch me. He saw to that."

"Do you have children, Roger?"

"Yes, three."

"Are they rich."

"Yes, Uncle Fitz saw to that also."

"Do they know it?"

"Not yet."

"When will you tell them? How will you tell them?"

"Wish I had the right song to sing them."

"That's what Betsy wants from us, isn't it?

"The right song to sing them."

CHAPTER 19

AIDS and Avarice

Avery and Ernesto sat together during lunch, exchanging their worlds. Conversation continued as they strolled to the lobby and found chairs in the corner.

Avery quietly described her life in Africa, her work, her husband and their children. She was disarmingly matter-of-fact about the squalor and the suffering, but not so graphic that Ernesto wished she would change the subject.

Not once did Avery mention her sacrifice or frustrations, her family's deprivations and dangers. Matter-of-factly she described their response to overwhelming need, continuing her family's tradition of medical service to the African poor and sick.

Ernesto was deeply embarrassed to disclose his grasping ambition—embarrassed to admit his burning desire to become rich and powerful, in part to prove himself and in part to please his mother. He had been "called" by these wealthy Chinese, trained and educated to do their bidding and now to profit by it. He was to own his own company, make his own mark, his own fortune, his own reputation. He was responding to the global market forces that had propelled him to the threshold of personal success.

So near the pinnacle self-doubt was setting in. Was he plucked from the cook's quarters, given an education he could never afford, employed by Chinese business geniuses, and sold one of their companies at a bargain price, just to become rich? Behind his calm and competent machismo mask, Ernesto was desperately searching for meaning to his ambition.

How strange to hear himself confiding all this to a black missionary physician he barely knew, who said very little in reply or rebuttal but who listened with such palpable concentration and kindness. Out it came, all of it without holding back, words Ernesto had said to no one before, thoughts he had not admitted to himself.

Avery looked pained.

"We too, are at a crossroads, Ernesto.

"Working for the Gates Foundation is not a financial sacrifice. Gates physicians are well paid. In less than two years my husband and I can retire on handsome annuities for the rest of our lives. Our children's educations are paid for, our own financial security is assured.

"It's a hard choice, Ernesto. Tikka begs us to send her home to U.S. schools. She knows we can afford it. We don't want to be separated from her. But if we force her to stay in Africa, she may resist her call if it comes.

"If we go home to be with her, are we rejecting our own calls?

"If we didn't have the money all of us would stay in Africa. God's will would seem much clearer if we couldn't afford the alternatives."

Ernesto pulled a paper from his pocket and read FitzWillard's musings aloud.

"Now, what was it Betsy wanted us to talk about?"

Both laughed as they strolled together down the hall towards the Pow Wow Room.

CHAPTER 20

Sallie and Fred

Sallie and Fred remembered each other. They had been awkward friends of sorts at Camp Denim, two very unhappy campers struggling to console each other and to be consoled. Had Sallie's hand found Fred's under the table when she reached for it during the morning session, his return squeeze might have updated their mutual consolation. Talking began as they walked from the dining hall back towards the Pow Wow Room. In Fred's presence, Sallie was unwinding, her sullenness fading, and her demeanor almost pleasant. Fred was at ease.

"I married three rich men, Fred. Two divorces made me rich. I'm in a good marriage now. If trust funds can make kids behave, my twins will be model citizens. The problem is, they're totally indifferent to money. They even compete to see who can live on less. Neither even *wants* a car! They wear used clothes from charity shops, bring home stuff left on the street, poke through refuse like it was sales merchandise.

"Drives me crazy. My husband thinks it's funny. That makes me crazier!"

They entered the Pow Wow Room and sat down. Fred began:

> "Until Africa, I wasn't sure why I was a physician. The responsibility is enormous, the risks are huge, the hours killing. I'm always, always tired, and getting grumpy like my stepfather—he was a physician. He's dead now. It's strange how I still admire him."

Sallie's voice managed genuine concern.

"Fred, how do you stand it?"

He sighed, then smiled boyishly showing deep dimples.

> "My anchor to windward is home. Kenneth and I have been together for eighteen years. It's a wonderful relationship.

> "Each of us has a daughter. We're biological fathers. Mine is six years old; Kenneth's is four. Our girls have the same biological mother, although her identity is secret—a very intelligent, healthy woman who donated eggs for in vitro fertilization. We found a wonderful surrogate mother who lent us her uterus twice. We were present for both deliveries. I assisted. Both little girls are already talking about Camp Denim.

> "Sallie, we're supposed to talk about money."

Sallie laughed out loud.

"I already have. Weren't you listening, Dr. Fred? My twins are money averse. What does it say in Betsy's fortune cookie?"

Same Sallie, mused Fred. Always an edge. Fred produced the FitzWillard quotations. Sallie scowled as she read aloud.

"It's a struggle to get rich by divorce? I'm not proud of it but I'm not ashamed either. I just hope my twins will find less humiliating ways to riches! They act as if money doesn't exist! How can I teach them to manage money if they won't *spend* it!

"I talk to them about money all the time. They just don't listen. They know where the money came from—their father (my ex-) reminds them constantly. They know they'll be supported through college. I'm not inclined to give them more until I die."

Fred looked away absently.

> "Kenneth has a trust fund. He's never worked, never had to, never wanted to work. Neither did his father. Kenneth works hard caring for our daughters. I'm not sure I'd have the patience. He does all the cooking and housework himself with no help. Says it makes him feel really needed and responsible for once in his life.
>
> "Kenneth could spend loads of money on us all but he doesn't. His parents lavished him with everything but themselves. He felt rejected, isolated, alone. Being gay didn't help. Kenneth is very giving. He wants to be there for the girls and for me. He wants to give them allowances

but they're too young. They do chores though—
and have to sit in 'time out' if they don't finish.

"Sometimes when I come home from late
rounds at the hospital worn out and in a foul
mood, Kenneth says I should just quit medicine
and let him support us all. It's tempting. Or was
tempting—until Africa.

"The girls know we live well. In time they'll
know how well. In time, we'll try to teach them
what money buys and what it can't. In time, we'll
try to help them with social responsibility."

Suddenly Fred's face twisted as though in pain:

"Oh God, Sallie, those little girls in Africa! So
many die as infants. So many die of diseases our
children never face. So many malnourished, sick,
facing early death. So many who survive will see
their own daughters die! And we worry about
our daughters becoming 'socially responsible'
about more wealth than they can ever spend!"

This time Sallie reached and found Fred's hand.

Then both hands.

CHAPTER 21

Reconvened

Betsy detected a different mood in the Pow Wow Room.

No one was talking. Fred sat next to Sallie, his arm across the back of her chair. They were smiling at each other. Ernesto wore a worried look, Avery a thoughtful one. Roger was expressionless. Connie entered without expletive and sat with both red-booted feet on the floor.

Betsy planned to greet them with another multimedia montage but their somber faces changed her mind. Instead she waited for someone to break the silence but none did. All looked at her as though asking her to say the first words.

"Was Skipper's speech that hypnotic?"

A few smiles, but no words yet.

"Too much good camp food?"

Fewer smiles.

"Give me a word or two describing your conversations after lunch?"

There was a long silence finally broken by Roger:

"Heavy."

And Avery:

"Troubling."

Connie:

"Yeah, heavy and troubling."

Sallie:

"Inconclusive."

Fred:

"Cathartic."

Ernesto:

"Full of guilts."

Betsy continued:

"Let me be up front with each of you. I thought we would have a fun discussion. I hadn't planned to get into heavyweight money matters but it seems we're headed that way. Don't let me put you on the spot but does anyone want to tell me what you talked about?"

No response. "OK," thought Betsy, "talk about yourself."

"My great grandfather escaped the Chinese communists in 1949. He left with nothing. He made it to San Francisco and started selling from a pushcart. At first his family scraped by on very little. He was uneducated but his children studied hard, won scholarships, took advanced degrees. His sons formed a business. Together they networked with other expatriate Chinese families first in San Francisco then Indonesia, Malaysia, the Philippines and Hong Kong.

"When China reopened for trade their sons built branches in Taiwan and Shanghai. My father, uncles, brothers and their Chinese associates own significant shares in the Panama Canal Company. Their network is big in South America. My generation hasn't struggled like our great grandfather. We haven't been up against it, back to the wall, survive or die. Somewhere I read that healthy wheat won't grow well in a greenhouse because it needs to struggle against the wind to be strong."

> "The wind blows pretty strong on this poor shock of wheat!"

It was Connie:

> "I live in bubble wrap just like a rich kid . . . ."

Betsy detected a decidedly different mood.

> " . . . that protects my voice from heat and cold. Protects my privacy from goon reporters and adoring fans."

Roger interrupted:

> "But you *made* it, Connie. You aren't some spoiled trillionheir."

Connie almost snarled,

> "Dammit, Roger, I didn't *earn* it! It was *given* to me.
>
> "I spin songs into money just like Rumple-what's-his-face spun straw into gold.
>
> "It's a goddam struggle! I inherited a *voice*."

Avery rose and said softly:

> "Thank you for sharing your great gift, Connie."

Connie stared at Avery for a long moment, then stood. The others braced for an ugly scene. Connie walked towards Avery, searched her face, then embraced her without a word and sat down. The room was quiet for a very long moment.

Then Sallie said:

> "I was accepted to a top college along with some of my classmates, but didn't get a scholarship. My parents said I couldn't go because we didn't have the money. We had a terrible argument.
>
> "My mother started cataloging the financial sacrifices they had made for me. 'We even had to get you a scholarship to that Camp Denim!' she screamed.
>
> "It was horrible!"

Sallie's voice began to waiver:

> "I married two rich men I couldn't love. Had

twins by the second. Talk about struggle—try divorcing a wealthy man! Their lawyers are savages! And the cruelest cut of all: after all my struggles for money, my twins act as though money doesn't exist!"

Fred asked:

"Do they know the story you've just told us?"

"No."

"Do you think it would help if they did?"

Betsy interrupted:

"What do the rest of you think? Sallie's twins are seventeen."

Roger:

"I can't think of a downside."

Connie:

"Sounds like those little rebels are trying to get Mom to lighten up about the long green. You're sellin' money angst and they ain't buyin'. I don't blame them. Maybe you ought to join 'em, Sallie. Go minimal yourself. Get yourself a double-wide trailer, buy a sorry old pickup truck, a bunch of my recordings and a used chenille bathrobe. Feed 'em grits, gravy and biscuits three times a day. They'll bolt for Gucci and Mercedes."

All laughed, even Sallie.

It was Avery:

> "Sallie, your story makes me very uncomfortable."

Betsy tensed.

Where was Avery going with this? Betsy remembered being emotionally undone by the pitiful wasted child in Avery's videomail. Was it Avery's turn to make them feel guilty about their own wealth, about their own healthy children?

> "Tikka begs us to send her home to U.S. schools. And she knows we can *afford* it. We don't want to be separated from her. But if we insist she stay in Africa we don't know how she might act out her disappointment.
>
> "As I told Ernesto, my husband and I feel a strong religious calling to our work in Africa. We don't know how our daughter would react to schooling in America. Nor do we know how she would react if we refused to send her. If we didn't have the money I'm sure all of us would stay in Africa. Our children would certainly understand if we didn't have the money to educate them in the States."

Ernesto interrupted:

> "It's the damned *choices*, Avery!
>
> "My mother didn't *choose* to work for Betsy's parents. It was the best job she could find. She had a son to raise.
>
> "I really didn't *choose* to go to business school.

Betsy's family made me a proposition I couldn't refuse. They overpaid me to work for them.

"Now I'm buying a company from them so I can get rich on my own. So my three little boys can have all sorts of *choices* that money can buy them. How do I know they will choose well? How do I know that they won't be immobilized by all those choices as old Fitz warned?

"If God isn't helping Avery choose Africa or the States, how can I help my boys choose? If money is coming between Avery and God, is money going to separate me from my boys?!"

Betsy stood.

"Ten minutes?"

No one left the room.

Sallie spoke:

"We can handle it, Betsy. I think we're getting somewhere."

CHAPTER 22

Money and Meaning

"All right, Avery. You have the floor."

Statuesque, somber, earnest, Avery began:

> "We've been talking about ourselves most of the
> time. And that's important.
>
> "How can we teach our children until we know
> ourselves? I don't know what to teach my children
> about money because I don't really know what
> money means to me. Perhaps I'm teaching them
> that I'm confused about money's meaning,
> money's place in my life, the place money should
> occupy in their lives.
>
> "Look, I'm a missionary kid. I grew up around
> indigenous people in Africa who had very, very
> little. Maybe they earned $50 a year, borrowed

or bartered for what they needed and mostly did without. Their lives were short and hard and brutish. Most were HIV positive. Until very recently, most of their babies were born HIV positive.

"We in the hospital compound lived like royalty. Clean running water, hot and cold, flush toilets, sturdy houses, plenty of nourishing food, servants to cook, clean and serve, and excellent medical care. No HIV.

"Our children grew up in the same environment. On their videophones they see another world they long for. My parents were good physicians and people of strong religious faith. They convinced us that our African world was much more important than the videophone world. They taught us that the indigenous people needed us and that God had sent us there to help them. They deeply believed they had no choice but to work there until God sent them elsewhere.

"Our parents couldn't *afford* to leave Africa until they retired in their seventies. We went to college and medical school on scholarships that obligated us to work in Africa for ten years after our training. And we didn't complain because, like our parents, God was sending us back to Africa.

"Tikka isn't sure she wants to be a physician. She isn't sure she wants to live in Africa. She isn't at all sure that God would send her there. We aren't as sure about her career as my parents were about my career. Perhaps we lack my parents' faith, their sense of calling.

"Oh dear. I started talking about our children but talked about us instead.

"I'm sorry."

Fred interrupted:

"Forgive me, Avery, is old man Gates really the devil trying to tempt you and your husband and your children away from God's work in Africa?"

Avery winced.

"Is money intrinsically evil?

"Is that what your asking, Fred?"

Fred sighed.

"I guess so."

Betsy intervened:

"Can we talk about the morality of money without religious connotations?"

Avery:

"Of course. Let's hear from FitzWillard."

Sallie blurted:

"First, let's hear from FitzSallie! My mother deceived me about money. I don't think she was evil. She was just ashamed . . . ashamed of what she couldn't give me. Ashamed of her abiding embarrassment because my father couldn't earn enough money for me to run with the rich friends she wanted me to have."

"And you Sallie?" asked Fred.

Anticipating an emotional explosion, the others changed positions and braced. Sallie thought for a long moment then responded quite composed:

"I wonder if I was still fighting Mother's battles in those divorce courts. Maybe I sued for big settlements so Mother could get out from under her shame. Maybe I'm most ashamed of how Mother's shame played out through me."

Roger asked:

"How did your mother react to your divorces?"

Sallie bowed her head.

Fred whispered:

"Sallie's mother has Alzheimer's. She hasn't recognized Sallie for several years."

Roger heaved a great sigh and began:

"Sallie, I wish I had as much insight about my mother as you have about yours. My mother was a chronic over-spender. My father's income couldn't keep up with her spending. When the money and credit were gone, she drank."

Betsy:

"Was spending an addiction, Roger?"

> "Exactly. So was alcohol. Spending addiction and alcohol addiction can be closely related. Her brother—Uncle Fitz—and my father laid down the law to her. Either she pulled herself together or she faced divorce and bankruptcy."

"How is she now?"

> "In remission on both counts but never cured of course. Only recovering. Alcoholics Anonymous referred her to Debtors Anonymous. Both use the Twelve Step program. She still goes to local meetings of both organizations. Her spending may be the hardest to control. She can give up alcohol completely but she must continue to spend."

Betsy:

"So money can make you sick?"

Fred:

> "I don't think so.
>
> "Money doesn't make you sick.
>
> "It may be the medium in which the sickness thrives. It may be the metaphor . . ."

Betsy:

"*Medium? Metaphor?* I thought the love of money is the *root* of all evil?"

Everyone seemed to speak at once. Betsy waited patiently until the noise subsided, then she spoke:

"As far as I can tell, money *is* the medium in my family.

"Money may be my family's primary connection.

"We're joined at the wallet."

CHAPTER 23

Skipper's News

A searing siren summoned all inside.

Wind whipped great sheets of rain across Camp Denim. The lake was a white froth. Trees gyrated in wild dances strobe lit by lightning. Gathered at the window after a break, Betsy's group was gazing at the storm when Skipper Shaw entered.

"Folks," said Skipper gravely, "we have a problem."

"As you may know we sew locator sensors into all Camp Denim tee shirts. Helps us find campers who wander off now and then.

"When we sounded the weather siren a while ago, we told the computer to locate all the kids who came to the reunion. It found all but six: Sallie's twins, Fitz Ringgold, Tikka, Ming and Pepe.

"We've checked the usual places lost kids turn up but haven't found your six yet. Camp Security suspects they are together somewhere but under deep cover that our beam can't penetrate. We've relayed their locator data to a satellite but no response as yet. Got any ideas?"

Stunned parents joined Skipper at the table. Ernesto asked:

"Are you sure they're together?"

"Not certain," Skipper replied, "but Pepe's brothers bribed him to hike with the twins. Someone saw Ming and Tikka leave the dining hall together after lunch. Fitz was tagging along."

Betsy interrupted:

"I specifically asked Ming to make friends with Tikka and Fitz."

Sallie:

"My twins are city kids. They know zip about the outdoors."

Nearby lightning dimmed the lights, followed immediately by a thunder crack.

Fred:

"Think back. We were once all campers here. Where would we go that locator beams couldn't find us?"

Fred looked around the table. When his eyes reached Sallie it clicked:

"The Dungeon!!" both shouted at once. "The Dungeon!!"

Sallie:

    "Fred found it when we were campers.

    "Sometimes Fred and I would hide there to get away from our miseries—from the teasing."

Fred:

    "It's a cave!"

Skipper:

    "Where is it? Could you find it?"

Sallie:

    "We're sure as hell going to *try*!!"

The others followed Sallie out of the room.

CHAPTER 24

The Search

Waiting on the wide porch a man and woman wearing hard hats—members of the Mountain Rescue Team—distributed orange hooded slickers and flashlights, then lead the party to the picnic pavilion that sheltered Roger and Connie earlier that day.

"We're going to find that cave," said the muscular woman in shorts with "*MR1*" inscribed on her hard hat.

Her voice was firm and measured. She was taking charge.

"Who's been in there?"

Fred and Sallie raised their hands and stepped closer to *MR1* who switched on her head lamp and opened a laminated map of the area.

"Find it," she commanded.

Fred and Sallie studied the map. The others looked on anxiously.

> "Sallie, did we reach the Dungeon from the Tomahawk trail? Or was it from War Club?"

Skipper:

> "Those old trails haven't changed much since you were campers, but they lead in opposite directions.

> "Which one?"

MR1 glowered at Skipper who stepped back.

> "I'm not sure either," said Sallie. "Should we split up?"

MR2 spoke:

> "Anyone a doctor?"

Avery and Fred raised their hands.

> "Doctor M'am, you go with *MR1* and the lady who's been there. You'll follow Tomahawk."

> "Doctor Sir, you go with me and Skipper up War Club.

> "The rest of you can stay here or divide up and go with us, but if you come along you must do what we say—is that clear?

> "We'll keep in touch by videophone."

No one stayed behind.

Less lightning, thunder diminishing, steady drenching rain. As they approached the Tomahawk trailhead, *MR1* asked Sallie:

"How long a walk was it?"

"Maybe ten minutes."

"Any landmarks?"

"I'm trying hard.

"I remember the entrance was downhill from the trail. And we crossed a stream just before we turned off . . . ."

MR1 scowled: "Streams are everywhere from this rain."

" . . . and there was a huge oak tree curved like a pregnant woman with a huge butt.

"Fred and I called it 'Big Mama'."

"Could you see the tree from the trail?"

"I think so. It was very near the entrance."

MR1 relayed Sallie's recollections to *MR2* on the videophone.

"Roger, *MR1*. Doc Sir says there's a big rock outcrop above the cave entrance about chest high.

"He remembers the stream and the Big Mama tree.

"He thinks the entrance isn't more than fifty feet off the trail.

"Have the state police sent up a search drone yet *MR1*?"

"Not a chance until the weather improves. Keep me posted."

Twenty minutes later, *MR1* called *MR2* on the videophone.

"We think we've found the cave *MR2*. We're about a quarter mile up Tomahawk. Better get over here. Look at this."

MR2 squinted at the picture on his videophone as the others gathered around. Behind a giant curved tree lay fresh earth and rock . . . from a recent landslide.

CHAPTER 25

A Visitation

Notwithstanding the weather a huge helicopter appeared overhead shining bright spotlights through the rain on the group gathered below. Its deep penetration radar had located a cavity in the rock structure and something moving inside emitting heat. It could be an animal den, but . . .

All shielded their eyes as the crew lowered a large orange machine in a cargo net. The machine reached the ground in a clearing near the bystanders. Very quickly two men in orange hard hats appeared at the helicopter's open door, climbed into a small cage and began their descent.

To relieve the tension from the blinding lights through rain, Betsy looked down, shut her eyes, rubbed them, and then opened slowly. She thought she saw the figure of a disoriented child staggering towards her in the wet, noise and glare. "Get a grip!" she said to herself. "I'm hallucinating." But the apparition persisted, lurching unsteadily like the emaciated African child in the videomail from Avery and Fred.

Ernesto felt a tug at his pocket. Thinking it was a bramble he moved away. A second tug. He looked down. It was a boy covered with mud and scratches, some bleeding, his soundless lips trying to say "Papa". As Ernesto lifted Pepe in his arms both began to cry. Other parents gathered around them. Pepe brought a precious message—their children hadn't suffocated . . . yet.

MR1 and *MR2* administered first aid. Clinging to his father, Pepe told them he had gone to pee and got lost. He found a hole in the rocks where he heard thunder. He dug around the hole until he could wriggle through and found himself outside under a huge tree where he huddled until he heard the helicopter and saw its lights. He had lost his flashlight. Would his brothers be angry? The others? They were too big to crawl through the hole.

The orange machine and its orange crew made short work of the debris blocking the entrance to the cave. Five thoroughly frightened but happy children were soon reunited with their thoroughly frightened and harried parents. All returned to Camp Denim for dry clothes, a late dinner and a night of rest.

Sallie slept between her twins in the king size bed in her large corner room. Pepe slept next to his father, his brothers in the other bed. Tikka and Avery talked and prayed late into the night. Fitz Ringgold wore his father's pajamas with the crest over the pocket. Ming insisted that Betsy leave lights on. Skipper invited *MR1* and *MR2* to the penthouse where they drank beer late into the night.

CHAPTER 26

Debriefing

With great difficulty Betsy rose early the next day and sat at a small study table. She shuddered at the thought of the near catastrophe of the night before. Ming slept soundly.

What a reunion! Her plans for a comfortable chat about "raising rich kids" transmogrified into group soul-searching she wasn't equipped to lead. Then the Dungeon—her worst nightmare had almost materialized!

Betsy had a strong impulse to cancel the scheduled Sunday morning session. She certainly wasn't going to leave Ming's sight and expected (correctly) that the others wouldn't leave their children.

At breakfast Betsy announced that the class on raising rich kids would continue in the Pow Wow Room and that children would be welcome, along with the Camp Denim psychologist, Dr. Nether, who insisted on being there.

All came. Dr. Nether invited each child to talk about the cave experience. Pepe told of crawling through the hole towards the thunder. Brad and Katelyn, the twins, felt very guilty about organizing the hike, apologizing profusely to children and parents, who responded in words and tones that said no apology was necessary.

Fitz Ringgold admitted he was terrified the entire time and felt ashamed for not being brave like Tikka. It was Fitz who found Pepe's *linterna*. Its light made waiting for rescue much more bearable.

Ming thanked Tikka for her strength, her prayers and steady encouragement to the others. The other children responded in words and tones that said Tikka prevented panic. Tikka thanked Ming for inventing the "money messages" game to pass the time.

To play "money messages" one player described an imaginary gift. The others tried to guess the hidden message the giver intended and how the receiver interpreted, or misinterpreted, the hidden message.

> In the cave, Pepe who at age six didn't really understand the game, told the others that his brothers had given him the *linterna* just that afternoon. Pepe said they gave him the flashlight because they wanted him to see in the dark. Fitz Ringgold giggled as he deciphered the brothers' money message: *"scram!"*

Pepe's brothers looked puzzled until Ernesto translated "scram" for them, then they giggled too.

> In the cave, Fritz Ringgold told of a gift from a father to his son. It was a very expensive and elaborate toy bank. A computer chip in the little

bank kept "accounts" and linked it to the Internet.
The father "deposited" his son's weekly allowance
in the toy bank by swiping a plastic card. The
chip automatically allocated each electronic
deposit between savings, charity, and
discretionary spending accounts in preset
proportions. The chip also tracked the boy's
predetermined "budget" for discretionary
spending. By swiping his plastic card, the boy
could "spend" electronically within his budget.
Any excess spending required a swipe of his father's
card, and that required a father-son discussion.
Other children in the cave puzzled over the
father's silent money message. One suggested "*be
smart about money*". Another guessed the message
received was "*father doesn't trust you*". Another
guessed that Fitz indeed had such a toy bank. He
did.

Roger Ringgold leaned forward to speak, but Dr. Nether raised a
hand.

"Let's withhold parents' comments for now."

In the cave, Tikka had told how an African girl
was awarded her own videophone as a prize for
graduating first in her class. In honor of her
achievement, the manufacturer also waived the
annual usage fee for three years. The videophone
was powered by solar batteries and connected
wirelessly to communications satellites. She could
communicate with other videophones anywhere
in the world, browse the Internet, and watch an
infinite variety of entertainments, all without
leaving her village that had neither telephones nor
electric power. People in her village were very

poor and many were sick. The girl yearned to live like the people she saw on her videophone, yearned to visit them, to know them, to be like them. Ming guessed the manufacturer's "money message" was either *"leave your village"* or *"change your village."* Brad thought the message received was *"get your neighbors to buy a videophone."* Katelyn offered that it was *"stay in your village and avoid boredom."*

The other parents didn't look at Avery, who was looking at the floor.

In the cave, Ming told the story of a rich boy whose family lived in a castle guarded by soldiers. Sometimes his Nanny would disguise him in peasant clothes, slip him past the guards, and take him with her to the town outside the castle walls. In the town he played (and sometimes fought) with other boys, made friends with peasant children, and learned how the townspeople hated the family in the castle. The townspeople circulated awful stories about his family that weren't true. When something went wrong in the town, the townspeople found ways to blame his family in the castle. What was the "money message" in Nanny's gift? One guessed, *"people hate you just because you're rich."* Another, *"money makes you a prisoner."* And another, *"the rich are captive, the poor are free."*

Betsy smiled broadly at Ming. They often teased about being "the princess in the castle."

In the cave, Brad and Katelyn described a dream about a brother and a sister running to catch their mother who kept dropping presents in their path. Sometimes they stumbled over the presents, sometimes tripped and fell. If they stopped to open the presents they might never catch her, so they didn't. Tikka asked if this was a real dream. It was. Both twins had dreamt it . . . often. Could there be a "money message" in a dream? Ming ventured that the mother used gifts to keep her children away from her. Tikka wondered if the children needed space from their mother. Fitz said that was stupid because in the dream the twins were trying to catch their mother and she was trying to get away from them. "That's why dreams are so crazy," said Katelyn. "Maybe the dream's money message is upside down." She turned to Brad, "Are we trying to push Mom away when we're awake, but trying to catch her when we're asleep?" "Yeh," Brad replied, "maybe she dreams she's chasing us and we're the ones tossing gifts in her path. Dreams are so weird!"

Seated between her twins, Sallie smiled and squeezed their knees.

CHAPTER 27

Money Messages

Dr. Nether called on Skipper to make an announcement.

> "Folks, there was some real excitement yesterday. I'm so thankful we managed a happy ending. I can't say enough about the Mountain Rescue Team. They're real pros! The helicopter spent the night on our soccer field. *MR1* and *MR2* are outside and would like to take the kids down there to meet the crew. You parents can join them later if you wish."

Of course the children wanted to go, and reluctantly their parents consented. As soon as they had left the room with Pepe in the lead, Dr. Nether turned to the parents.

"It was important to let your children talk about yesterday's experience in front of you and each other. It's an experience they won't forget, nor will you I'm sure. They may also experience some psychological fallout—fears, nightmares, flashbacks, that sort of thing. If so, it might be a good idea to contact your therapist. If you don't have one, Camp Denim can refer.

"Betsy tells me your session on 'raising rich kids' got pretty involved yesterday. Given what's happened with your children, she and I would understand completely if you wanted to close the book on that part of your reunion.

"On the other hand after hearing your kids describe their game, there may be some loose ends you want to talk about. Betsy has briefed me about your sessions yesterday. What's your pleasure?"

Through the picture window in the Pow Wow Room they watched the band of children walking and skipping towards the soccer field laughing and talking with great animation. Skipper was in the lead, *MR1* and *MR2* bringing up the rear. When they were out of sight Sallie said,

"I'll start, Dr. Nether. Can you interpret the twins' dream?"

Nether chuckled,

"Dreams can be pretty crazy, can't they? Therapists are fascinated by dreams but we can only speculate about their 'meaning'. My hunch is that you and your twins have some unresolved issues about gifts or money that's distancing them from you, and they aren't comfortable with that distance.

"On the surface your twins may be having fun acting out their pretended aversion to money. Deeper down they may suspect you're genuinely hurt by their behavior. Perhaps their dream is a goofy way of draining off their anxiety about hurting you—a kind of psychological pressure relief valve. I really don't know what their dream 'means', but I suspect its origin is in an anxiety they share about you."

"Sallie, can I ask you a somewhat delicate question?"

"Sure . . ."

"Do you think their behavior is funny . . . humorous?"

"Their stepfather certainly does."

"Do you ever joke with your twins about their money minimalism?"

"No."

"I saw you pinch their knees while the kids were talking about their dream. What did you mean about that pinch? Was that a humorous pinch?"

"Well . . . not really. I wanted to pinch them much harder but it wasn't appropriate under the circumstances."

"Could those pinches be the beginning of some gentle teasing about their lifestyles?

"Not disapproval, certainly not censure.

"Just gentle teasing?"

Connie interposed:

"Sure, Sallie.

"I'll bet you're real fun when you're not so up

tight. Just relax your sphincters and get down with the Clearasil crowd."

The others' chuckling ceased as Sallie turned sternly to face Connie who returned a stern look in kind. One or the other began to grin. Then both collapsed in laughter until tears came.

"Connie, I'm writing that down. May I quote you?" asked Dr. Nether.

More laughter.

"Anything else, Sallie?"

> "Yes. What do you suppose the kids express with their 'street people' imitations?"

"I wouldn't know without talking with them.

"One thing: I wonder if they're involved in a kind of reverse elitism.

"Are they setting themselves apart from their peers in a kind of clique?"

> "I really don't know," said Sallie.

> "If they have friends that don't share their lifestyle I don't know them."

Betsy interjected:

> "Dr. Nether, is it possible that they have adopted 'disguises' so they won't be picked out of a crowd as rich kids?

"Does their lifestyle give them more mobility in the world? Like the Nanny in Ming's story who dressed the prince like a peasant?"

"I think it depends on how they use their 'disguises'. If they don't interact with people who aren't rich, then it sounds more like an elite clique.

"If they initiate genuine contacts with poor and underprivileged people and their dress makes those contacts easier, then I see more substance to it."

Sallie:

"I know they get their clothes from charity shops. I don't know if they make friends with poor people."

"Would you approve or disapprove if they did?"

"Before this weekend I would have disapproved.

"But that sounds like my mother, doesn't it.

"Perhaps I need to find out more about what they're doing . . . if they'll tell me."

"Anything else, Sallie?"

"No, other than I need to get Connie's videophone number."

"Roger, you started to say something after your son Fitz finished. Want to say it now?"

"I feel pretty stupid about the toy bank.

"Maybe I'm afraid Fitz will be irresponsible like my mother and I want to protect him from that.

"Do you suppose he thinks I don't trust him?"

"Is he fairly trustworthy for a boy of nine?"

"I think so. He's pretty responsible."

"But not as responsible as you were at nine?"

"When I was nine years old I had to be a grownup. My mother was the child."

"How does Fitz handle money?"

"Well, he doesn't get much allowance.

"He spends it mostly for stuff that appeals to nine-year-olds."

"Do you and Fitz talk about money? Ever disagree about money?"

"No. He doesn't ask for more."

"We think children establish their attitudes towards money between ages eleven and fourteen.

"My guess is that you can teach Fitz some basic money habits at his present age, but it will be two years or more before his attitudes will begin to shape.

"If the toy bank is fun for him and for you I see nothing wrong with using it to handle his allowance. Be prepared that his younger brothers may have different reactions, though.

"You might check yourself about pushing him into adulthood prematurely. Just because you had to be a grownup at his age doesn't mean it's healthy for him. He needs to be a kid."

"When do you think I should tell him about his grandmother's spending?"

"Does he suspect?"

"I don't think so."

"He really wouldn't understand in the way you want him to understand at this age. Maybe a few years from now would be better, if at all."

"Anyone else?"

"Not for me," said Betsy, "unless you see something ominous lurking behind our games of 'princess in the castle'."

Dr. Nether smiled.

"No. Is Ming surrounded by security people like you were at her age?"

"Security is even tighter for Ming . . . but it's less obvious.

"More electronics intruding, fewer people."

"Anyone else?"

No one looked at Avery who was deep in thought.

"Dr. Nether, is Tikka sending me a money

message in her story about the African girl and the videophone?"

"What do you think, Avery?"

"I think we'll need to talk about it, don't you?"

"Yes I do.

"I think her story would be a great place to begin your conversation. Will your husband participate?"

"Can we wait that long?"

"I think so. Tikka will have lots to tell him. You and he will find the right time and place to talk with Tikka about her story."

Dr. Nether looked around the table and sensed closure.

"Well, let's go visit those heroes down on the soccer field."

CHAPTER 28

Betsy's Diary

January 4, 2033

Well . . . some of us may not remember Skipper's lottery ticket, but none of us will *ever* forget our 30th Reunion at Camp Denim. Thank goodness for Mountain Rescue . . . and for Dr. Nether who rescued me!

So far Skipper has kept the story away from the media. Camp Denim doesn't need that publicity, nor do we or our children. All of us agreed not to talk about it beyond our immediate families. Each of the children wrote a letter to Mountain Rescue before we left. Each child received a warm handwritten reply signed by *MR1* and *MR2*. I still don't know their real names.

Several times since, I've sat down to write up that experience for my dissertation on The Healthy Wealth Movement. It's hard to include something so personal and so traumatic.

Ming and I have had several long talks about the reunion. So far I haven't seen any of the symptoms Dr. Nether mentioned. Our therapist says to keep an eye on her for a while. Ming was really impressed by Sallie's twins . . . that they may have found a way to slip out of the palace. Ming wants to dress in denim as a disguise. Who knows, she may make a fashion statement. I worry that Ming is isolated by our wealth. Ming was *really* impressed by Tikka and is devouring books about Africa. Her science fair project deals with the social impact of the AIDS vaccine. She and Dr. Fred have been exchanging videomails.

As far as the others, I'll just attach their videomails.

From Fred:

Fred was sitting at his desk wearing a white physician's coat.

"Hi, Betsy! Hope you and your children have a great holiday. Kenneth and I and the girls are staying close to home this year, sort of hunkered down even though they weren't trapped in that cave.

"First let me thank you for getting us together to talk about money. Kenneth and I have been pretty vague about the 'money messages' we send each other and the girls overhear. We're more careful to say what we mean now and to double check what we think we hear.

"Instead of gifts to each other, Kenneth and I contributed to medical relief agencies in Africa. I plan to help Avery again next summer if she'll have me around. I keep literature about third world medical needs in our waiting rooms and donate part of all patient fees directly to that work. It's thrilling how some patients want to talk about Africa before their symptoms.

"You surely started some conversations that were long overdue. Kenneth has had several discussions with his parents. Thanks, Betsy. You did us all a real service."

Fred

From Roger:

Roger wore his elegant gray suit and burgundy tie. He sounded somber.

"Hi, Betsy.

"The fun weekend turned dramatic, didn't it. Neither of us expected a wrenching reunion.

"Fitz is having some nightmares and has been pretty "clingy" since we returned home. It may be difficult to coax Fitz into a cave any time soon.

"I told Fitz we needn't use the bank for his allowance but he insists. The other cave kids wanted videomail pictures of it. We're being more playful about what he gets and spends.

"Spent some quality time with my mother over the holidays. Things were less tense between us. She noticed and said so. Mom's holding her own although she overspent on Christmas presents for our boys. She went to a Debtors Anonymous meeting on New Year's Eve.

"Sorry you folks had to share those scars from my childhood. I didn't anticipate a public exorcism of my personal demon. You were very kind and patient with me. Thanks."

Roger

"P.S. Connie opened a very nice new account at our cyberbank."

From Sallie:

"Betsy, I wish I could tell you that everything is great but everything's about the same. The twins still look like skid row, only clean. They still won't drive or spend. They still have the same friends.

"Katelyn is having a real guilt trip about the cave experience. Videomails from the other kids might help her get through it. Brad seems OK.

"I did tell the twins about my Camp Denim trauma as a sponsored kid. They listened respectfully and without much reaction. Maybe it will soak in eventually. They had a harder time with my angst about getting rich from divorces, especially from divorcing their Dad. Brad said he'd heard enough and left the room. Katelyn followed him crying. It was really grim around here for a while. Maybe they'll understand eventually. They needed to know . . . I guess. I did learn that they and some friends are volunteering in the food pantry in a homeless center and have been for some time.

"I had the same conversation with my husband. It went much better. I think he understands. Betsy, I planned to raise hell at the reunion and almost did. Thanks for being so understanding."

Sallie

From Ernesto:

"Hi, China Doll.

"My family spent a peaceful Christmas in Bogotá. It's very safe and peaceful here. Chinese army uniforms everywhere. Maria misses Cuba but I think she'll adjust . . . eventually.

"Pepe seems fine . . . forever draping a blanket over a couple of chairs begging his brothers to play 'cave'. They tease that he just wants another flashlight. Meanwhile, *I'm* the one who's having the bad dreams. Can you hug a little boy too much?

"Avery and I stay in touch. We're facing similar dilemmas you know, but Avery is much closer to God. That makes her predicament more difficult than mine.

"Maria and I have had several long conversations about my future. Most of all, Maria wants me to be a good husband and father and a good son to my mother. She says I don't need to become the biggest or the richest.

"Meanwhile your brothers send you their best regards from Columbia. They're making deals right and left."

Ernesto

From Avery:

"Hello, Betsy.

"After holidays in the States we're back home in Africa.

"None of us will ever forget that Camp Denim reunion! We think Tikka is OK about the cave . . . at least so far. She has discussed it with us several times. Each time she tells us how brave the other children were.

"Pepe gave them quite a scare when he disappeared. Fitz cried most of the time but apparently didn't panic. I'm so thankful they had *light* during that ordeal. Wasn't Ming creative about that 'money message' game! A regular little Betsy! Tikka was standing at the mouth of the cave during the landslide . . . she said it was just like a garage door closing from the bottom to the top.

"What Tikka hasn't talked with us about is the story she told about the African girl who won the videophone. I suppose she'll find the right time and place to tell us more.

"I've had the oddest thought lately. Remember how Plato illustrates his theory of ideas—people chained in a cave with their backs to the entrance. There's a bonfire outside. *Real* things pass between the bonfire and the cave entrance but the people inside only see shadows on the cave wall, never the real thing. Did you ever think of money as a *shadow* of real things? Maybe there's a 'money message' in that.

"We're no nearer resolving our dilemma about returning to the States. Our hope is that Tikka is doing some rethinking . . . and repraying. Our prayer is that she'll be called to change her village but we'll leave that in God's hands.

"Thank you so much for your important part in the reunion. In spite of the fright it was a real blessing to us all."

Avery

From Connie:

Connie was videomailing from her bus again. Again the rumble was partially covered by country music playing in the background.

A hand appeared holding a cosmetics brush.

"Lester, kindly refrain from applying my makeup just now, won't you? I'm having a little cyberspace chat with my Camp Denim friend, Betsy. Toodeloo, Lester.

"Off singin' to the troops again, Betsy. That was a real wahoo of a reunion. Hope all them young'uns are past their bad dreams. Between us girls I've had a few myself.

"By the way, you didn't walk off in my red boots did you Bets? I can't find them anywheres."

"Hang in there."

Connie

At the bottom of the diary page, Betsy noted:

"Just before leaving the reunion I went to the penthouse to tell Skipper goodbye. While he was dressing, I used the guest bathroom. Connie's boots were in the bathroom closet."

CHAPTER 29

Videochat

March 15, 2033

Betsy checked her makeup and straight black hair, faced the communications module, and began speaking.

"Hi, Dr. Nether. Thanks for your time."

> "Hello Betsy. Thanks for the update on your reunion."

"I guess I'm searching for what I've learned from that experience."

> "How can I help you?"

"Let's begin with the children one by one."

> "I'll call the role.

"At six, Pepe doesn't pay attention to money. At nine, Fitz is curious but not really interested. Your twelve-year-old Ming is very aware—didn't she originate the 'money messages' game in the cave? Tikka knows her parents have the means to move to the U.S.—she's fifteen. At seventeen, Sallie's twins are reacting to the dark side of money and divorce."

"Roger is trying to teach good money habits to Fitz."

"Roger was trying to push him across the money threshold too soon. I suspect Roger caught himself offloading sad baggage onto his son and stopped pushing."

"What do you think of the toy bank?"

"The toy bank may help Fitz establish good habits like saving and giving, but a toy can't build healthy money attitudes. That's his parents' job."

" . . . and parents don't get much help from the kids-and-money experts, do they! Most of them come across like FitzWillard clones: *Mom and Dad—step right up—get your cookie cutters for kids and cash—one size fits all!*"

"Indeed. What works for one family may not be healthy for another. It's important for parents to discover what *does* work. Kids don't acquire good money attitudes by osmosis. If parents don't *talk* about money their kids are candidates for FitzWillard's cave."

"FitzWillard's cave?"

"Yes, I imagine FitzWillard standing at the entrance to a dark cave, holding a lottery ticket in his hand, inviting a crowd of wealthy children inside for the kids' show."

"Ugh! Kids are bombarded from all sides to *buy stuff* that will make them the kind of person they want to be, or to *appear* to be. Just watch the kids' shows on the videophone."

"Remember "Let Money Solve Your Problems", *'Money is meaning!'* FitzWillard declared. *'Find wealth and you will find yourself! Once wealthy, your destiny becomes creative spending!'* Of course FitzWillard encouraged us to buy what FitzWillard had to sell."

"Are Sallie's twins rebelling against FitzWillardism?"

"It's closer to home, I think. Sallie's twins may be saying 'If money did that to Mom and Dad, we don't want it.' Or possibly 'we're afraid of money'."

"Was it wise for Sallie to tell them her money stories? Will it help them to know Mom's struggling too?"

"I think so but it may take time for them to understand and forgive her."

"Should Roger tell Fitz about his mother's compulsive spending?"

"Eventually perhaps, but not until Fitz is more mature and needs to know. That's Roger's judgment call."

"Speaking generally, do our children need to share our money stories?"

"I think so. Listen to this:

"Money is part of family heritage. In too many households, talking about family wealth with children is more taboo then sex discussions. To children, parents' refusal to talk about something suggests that the subject matter is dark or shameful.

"Treating family wealth as taboo almost assures that children will grow up uncomfortable with their wealth. Failure to talk about money sends the message to children that they are not trusted, a real blow to self-esteem.

"Children want to know where the money came from (whether from Mom or Dad), how large the fortune is, and how and when they are to receive some of it."

"Dr. Nether, you're quoting from FitzWillard!"

"I am, Betsy. There's some wisdom there. I was pleasantly surprised."

"Roger tells me "Let Money Solve Your Problems" was ghost-written by FitzWillard's henchmen as a marketing tool."

Dr. Nether glanced at her watch and took a sip of water.

"When the time comes Dr. Fred's daughters will hear very different money stories: Kenneth's family hasn't worked for two generations; Fred's donating money and medical skills to the third world. Eventually the girls will hear their fathers' larger stories. I'll wager that

Kenneth and Fred are already working on when and how to tell them.

"Money is an important part of their story—and of *every* parent's story. We don't need to be the heroes of our money stories. We don't need to be wise or even successful. Our mistakes, our failures are part of the whole story. Why try to deceive our kids about money? Ask Sallie about deceit."

"What about Ernesto?"

"An entrepreneur looks up from his work one day to discover his children grown and gone. The entrepreneur has been fiercely loyal to his favorite child: his company. I hope this won't be Ernesto's story. Ernesto doesn't have to choose between being a good father and a great business success. But he *must* choose to be *both*. I hope Ernesto will always feel Pepe tugging on his pocket."

"And Avery?"

"That's between Avery and God. I've not been invited."

"Tell me about your children, Betsy."

"My children?

"Ming and I joke about being the princess in the palace, but it isn't very funny.

"Dr. Nether, I've conducted dozens of interviews for this dissertation. I have a knack for getting people to talk about money, but my own father and uncles and brothers won't talk to *me* about it! 'Don't worry your pretty little head', sounds pretty weird in Chinese! Maybe that's why I chose to research the Healthy Wealth Movement. If my family won't talk to me about money I'll find out for myself! . . . And for Ming, of course.

"I opened Pandora's Box at Camp Denim, didn't I?"

> "Money conversations can get out of hand in a hurry no matter how innocent or well-intended. But you did your friends a real service, Betsy."

"I hope so. We were kids on the money threshold when Skipper John flashed that lottery ticket thirty years ago. Some of our childish responses were pretty serious, weren't they? Thirty years later we've won the lottery but we're still stumped by Skipper's question."

> "Isn't it ironic that it's time to teach our children before we know ourselves. At best we grow up along with them and we learn together with them. It's called parenting."

"So we and our children search together for answers to their money questions?"

> "I think so.

> "Aren't those the best answers, the answers you discover together?

> "Inside answers instead of outside answers."

"Shall I put that in my dissertation?"

> "Why not?"

Dr. Nether began to collect her things.

"Did you know that FitzWillard was working on another book when he died?"

"I didn't."

" . . . an expansion of his unpublished papers."

"Some of those ideas are quite incisive."

"They weren't *his* ideas."

"Really?"

"No, I did some digging.

"For years he interviewed FitzClients—parents and children—about money issues. The unpublished papers are summaries of his interview notes.

"He planned to publish *their* answers as *his* wisdom."

"Scoundrel to the end?!"

"Standing at the cave entrance—holding the lottery ticket."

"Betsy, this has been delightful. I look forward to reading your dissertation."

" . . . and thank you so much, Dr. Nether. I'll quote you carefully."

Betsy folded her notes.

" . . . . and by the way, Dr. Nether, do you follow country music?"

"No, should I?"

"Connie Alden's new song is moving up the charts.

"I heard her humming the tune at Camp Denim."

"What's the title?"

"*My Summer Children.*"

CHAPTER 30

Some Unpublished Writings of
F. Willard FitzWillard

Betsy copied these passages from FitzWillard. Her comments are in *italics*.

False Cocoon. "Money gives trillionheirs a false sense of security. You live wrapped in cotton, protected from the cold and heat. You have never been too cold or too hot. That's not good."

I wonder what would give me a real sense of security.

Is the best protection pretending you're not rich?

Like Ming's prince in the castle going to the town?

Are Sallie's twins wearing disguises to protect themselves? But from what?

My Money Or Me? "It's difficult for trillionheirs to value their accomplishments. You suspect your 'successes' are really due to wealth and position. It's hard to be sure you have achieved anything significant or that others really like you for yourself. Others resent your good fortune and their resentment stings you. Fear of failure runs high among inheritors especially if your father has been a huge success."

Fitz Willard opened bank doors for Roger.

Ernesto's mom built the launch pad and my family furnished the fuel.

Can Ernesto ever repay his mom? Can he pass his gratitude down to his boys?

Sallie's mother resented the families of Sallie's wealthy friends.

None of us "made it all on our own". So get used to it!

Everyone around that table at Camp Denim has "made it" but me!

Why Struggle? "The U.S. Army once challenged recruits to 'Be All You Can Be!'. You trillionheirs will never need to struggle in order to survive. You will never be driven by life's necessities. You will never know what you might have accomplished with your back to the wall without the family safety net. No one has devised a substitute for struggle, its lessons and benefits.

Can we become our best selves without struggle? Not having to struggle makes it hard for you to stick to your goals in the face of setbacks and frustrations. Too often your goals are ill-defined particularly your career goals. Too often your motivation is short-lived and lacks intensity. Self-discipline requires focused and sustained energy. Self-discipline requires you to postpone gratification for ultimately higher rewards. You need self-discipline not only for work but for significant human relationships. Lack of self-discipline is a major life-long cause of difficulty."

Can money prevent rich kids from becoming "all they can be"?

Can wealthy parents "synthesize" struggle for their kids?

Should they? Is that "tough love"?

Do we ransom our kids from struggle?

Can competitive sports supply struggle, goals and discipline?

How do we discipline our wealthy kids when everyone else indulges them?

The Power Curve. "You feel uncomfortable with the power of your wealth, since you haven't earned it and don't deserve it. You may deny or avoid your power. Or you may misuse power arbitrarily, run roughshod over other people—overcompensating for a sense of inadequacy and confusion. Either way others find it hard to work for you—and hard to live with you."

Gilt Guilty. "Guilt is rampant among trillionheirs. It's hard to accept unmerited good fortune. You may be consciously apologetic or arrogantly contemptuous—both are ways of coping with your unrecognized guilt feelings. The rich who didn't earn it crave a sense of entitlement that forever eludes them."

Wow, "I don't deserve it" was a constant theme in the Pow Wow Room!

If we didn't earn our money does that mean we don't deserve it?

Will we always chase "entitlement" to our good fortune and never find it?

Are we "undeserving rich" cursed to be uncomfortable with money?

Are we cowardly if we try to conceal that we're rich?

Lifts . . . but Separates. "If you were born to wealth, it's hard to understand the lives and experiences of persons in ordinary financial circumstances. You consort with peers at private clubs and join in expensive activities that exclude persons of ordinary means. But there's always a sense of alienation, that you are different from most people."

Too Rich for Troubles. "You will experience envy, anger and resentment from those not so privileged as you. Middle-income people find it hard to behave normally in the presence of the wealthy. They have a hard time feeling sympathy of any kind for the rich, who should be able to afford a constant state of bliss. Check the mass media for this public attitude."

Poor little princess, a prisoner in the castle!

Camp Denim was like being among the townspeople in disguise.

Weren't my parents wise to send me there!

I didn't even speak to Ernesto before Camp Denim.

He was the cook's boy.

Just listen to me!

Oops! I violated Camp Denim dogma.

I only invited rich people to my workshop!

Mea Culpa

But the wealthy are different!

Who else has rich kids?!

Too Many Choices? "Excessive options plague the wealthy. You have too many choices. Few trillionheirs cope successfully with all the options money can buy. Too many options can paralyze decision-making."

Avery's parents didn't think they had a choice about Africa.

God said go!

They thought they didn't have a choice to leave either.

Also didn't have the money.

Avery and her husband can afford to leave. Oh, God!

Fred has the option to quit medicine and do nothing.

Kenneth would gladly support him, probably encourage him.

Sallie's twins won't exercise the options Sallie's trying to give them.

Ernesto's anxious about too many choices and still bewildered why he was "chosen" by my family in the first place.

He hasn't come to terms with his good fortune.

"Why me?" cries Ernesto as though his good fortune were misfortune.

"All that money can buy" is quite an array.

Who Would I Be Without It? "Fear of losing wealth is prevalent but seldom conscious. 'What would I do if I had to support myself? Make my own way?' You may harbor a continuing fear of what might happen if the money disappears—I call this fear the 'bag-lady syndrome'. 'I would panic if I lost my money. I could never survive. I would die'."

Perhaps I Can't. "Fear of failure plagues all of us at times. As a result many inheritors won't face challenges because they are unsure they have what it takes to surmount them. This can be especially painful to a young person with an exceptionally successful father and whose parents have excessive expectations."

Money can't make us secure from the fear of losing it.

Who would we be without our money?

What would we do?

What would people think?

What a terrible loss of face!

Who would be our friends?

What would happen to our children?

Would I want to jump out a window?

Trillionheirs May Not Get Good Parenting. "Many wealthy parents unwittingly neglect their children. They are busy and active. They can afford household staff and boarding schools. But these are second-class surrogates. Surrogates can't provide the personal attention and caring that children want and need from their parents. If parental nurture is faulty or inadequate it's hard for children to deal with maturity and to become trusting. Rich parents may intrude excessively into the lives of their children. Their concern for the family fortune produces excessive interference in their children's lives."

Rich Parents May Have The Hardest Parenting Job. "Good child rearing is especially important for wealthy families. Good nurture requires lots of love, training, counsel and good examples by *both* parents through childhood and adolescence and beyond. Parents need to be very good listeners. While there is much emphasis on 'quality time', parents also need to be there when nothing seems to be happening. Strong parenting is important for all children. Strong parenting is particularly important for children who grow up with the paradoxical problems of a lifetime of financial security and comfort. Wealthy parents need to help their children through frustration and disappointments when there is great temptation to quit. Raising rich kids may be *a harder job* than raising kids who aren't so privileged."

Trillionheirs Will Parent Trillionheirs. "Raising your own children can free you from your own problems that accompany wealth. You can find great meaning in helping their children avoid the pitfalls and comfort in knowing that your grandchildren may also escape some of them.

"Poor little rich kids!"

I have friends who say they had two mothers: one white and one black.

Father took time with my brothers.

They were father's future business partners.

I was afraid to bother him. He was always so busy.

Father didn't know how bad my brothers behaved when he was gone.

I don't think my parents intruded into our lives.

They just had strict rules and our household staff enforced them.

Surrogates. "Though hired household staff live on the periphery of parents' lives they play a central role with children. Trillionheirs tell of deep pain suffered when beloved nannies suddenly disappeared or were terminated without explanation. Great care should be taken in selecting people to work in your household; monitor them closely. Trillionheirs report instances of cruelty and neglect by nannies never noticed by their parents or when reported were not taken seriously. Moreover, how parents treat household workers influences children in their future relationships with employees and other non-affluent people."

Important Others. "Young people have relationships with important other adults who may become role models for them— teachers, counselors, scoutmasters, coaches, family friends. Parents may have their own relationships with these 'important others' and should be careful not to show disapproval just because the adult friend comes from a different socio-economic background."

Ernesto's mom spoiled my brothers.

She was kind to me.

Her Cuban-Chinese dishes were divine!

Mother kept a close watch on our household workers.

She quizzed us regularly about them.

I remember she fired a few.

Don't remember being mistreated by any of them.

Mother ran a tight ship. Do I?

"Mirror, mirror on the wall, am I my Mother after all?"

Mmmm . . . talk to Ming about that.

Money See, Money Do. "Parents need to be comfortable, clear, and balanced about their own wealth, free both of pride and shame about it. Parents' unresolved problems about wealth could contaminate their children. The ways parents manage money inevitably teaches their children, for better or worse."

The Last Taboo. "In many affluent households talking about the family wealth with children is more taboo then sex discussions. To children, parents' refusal to talk about something suggests that the subject matter is dark or shameful. Treating the family fortune as taboo almost assures that children will grow up uncomfortable with their wealth. Failure to talk about money sends the message to children that they are not trusted, a real blow to self-esteem. Children want to know where the money came from (whether from Mom or Dad), how large the fortune is, and how and when they are to receive some of it."

It will take time for Sallie to get "comfortable, clear, and balanced" about her money.

It will take time for me, too.

I felt so ashamed after watching that African videomail from Avery and Fred.

Ashamed of what?

Ashamed that my family is rich? No.

Ashamed that my father is powerful? No.

Ashamed that I've taken our money for granted and been so glib about it? Getting close.

I don't envy Roger the task of explaining uncle FitzWillard to his boys.

Is explaining money to children like explaining sex?

Don't make them feel uncomfortable for being curious?

Answer their questions truthfully with responses they're able to understand at the time?

Wearing Wealth. "The art of spending is a neglected topic in many wealthy families. So also is the art of handling the position and influence that wealth makes possible. As always, parents need to lead by example, to point out how other families may be mishandling wealth, and to emphasize social responsibilities imposed on the wealthy."

Allowances. "Give children a regular allowance as a part of the child's right to a portion of the family fortune not connected with doing chores or good behavior and *not* subject to being withheld as punishment. The obligation to do chores should be a condition of belonging to the family rather than reimbursable services."

Summer Jobs. "As they grow older, real summer jobs help children learn that they could support themselves. It's best if children find their own jobs without help from their parents."

This is as close as FitzWillard comes to specific advice.

Is he pitching "creative spending"?

Leading by example is the hardest part!

Allowances? We just pay the children's bills.

That's their share of the family fortune. They have everything anyway.

Roger may have the germ of a good idea with the toy bank.

Make money fun!

Chores? Get real! Look at their rooms . . . if they'll unlock the door. Yuk!

I can't wait until they're old enough for summer jobs. Then the fun begins!

Do Sallie's twins work summers in a homeless shelter?

I wonder if Fred will take their girls to Africa some summer.

Would Kenneth allow it? Would Kenneth go too?

If Avery's family moves to the U.S., what will Tikka do during the summertime?

I wonder if Connie would hire Ernesto's boys to wash her bus.

Roots. "A sense of heritage pulls things together for trillionheirs. They need to feel good about where the money came from, good about the relatives who created and managed it. If the history of family wealth is cloudy, be candid about the unfortunate past and the family's clear commitment to use its present wealth in socially responsible ways."

We have a terrific family history.

Sorry my children won't hear great grandfather describe his escape from China.

Or his pushcart experiences in San Francisco.

My children won't learn much about our companies from the commercial videos.

The videos conceal much more than they reveal.

My children need to hear the inside stories from Father and the uncles.

We need family retreat . . . if we can get everyone in the same hemisphere at the same time.

Schools. "Choosing schools is very individual and very important. Often the choices are not easy, *e.g.* public vs. private, day school vs. boarding school. Intellectual, psychological and emotional factors all play an important part. It may be wise to bring in an educational consultant. It may not be wise to insist that children go to schools that their parents attended. Above all, children themselves should be actively involved in the choosing process."

Try being a lazy Chinese-American student!

Nobody believes you! Your parents least of all!

Study, study, study. Be the best. Lead the class!

Get degrees. Oh, yes, our daughter will become a PhD soon.

Bring home a "B" and you were punished.

Bring home a "B" and the family loses face.

My ancestors got where they are by being the best, the brightest, and the shrewdest.

Not a bad story to tell our children.

Intergenerational Estate Planning. "Transmitting wealth is complex and very individual. Of course it's important to minimize taxes, promote sound investments and protect the family fortune against bad judgment. But don't overlook the tricky ethical and psychological issues. Above all, *keep trillionheirs informed!* Insist on intergenerational estate planning that involves discussions between givers and potential inheritors. Estate planning in secret is deeply resented by most inheritors especially when they learn the details only after the death of a parent."

No one in my generation knows what the family owns except my oldest brother.

I don't know what I own. I just sign where told and vote as directed.

I haven't asked Brother for details but he's probably sworn to secrecy.

I'll ask him . . . ask for a meeting with Father and the uncles!

The princess wants to know what's in the treasury

I won't snitch! You can trust me.

A meeting with my parents about their wills?

"What do I get when you die . . . you who have given me everything?!

Building Character: Giving and Withholding. "Resist the temptation to manipulate behavior by promises of inheritance or disinheritance no matter how tempting and no matter how well those promises or threats seem to work. Locking a small child in the closet 'works'—except for deep psychological scars. So-called 'incentive trusts' can backfire. It's one thing to require a child to demonstrate financial maturity; it's quite another to force a child to forego his or her true nature just for the sake of an inheritance."

FitzWillard was wrong about controlling children's conduct with money.

"Find wealth and you will find yourself." That's hogwash . . . and he knew it!

Reward children with praise and encouragement.

Punish children with disapproval, disappointment and restricted freedom, but never deny love.

Don't substitute money for yourself.

Don't let money become just another surrogate between busy parents and their children.

Money can become a powerful control device . . . like a dark closet.

Equal Treatment. "Resist the strong impulse to treat children exactly equally. The genius of parenting is to understand the individual differences between our children and to respond appropriately. Equal isn't always fair and fair isn't always equal. For example: why should children who have no interest in the family business be given the same number of shares as children who will devote all their working lifetimes to the company? Inflexible equality almost always backfires sooner or later."

Love And Work: Basic Human Needs. "Career choices for trillionheirs are both difficult and crucial. Following father's footsteps can lead down a blind alley especially if father has been exceptionally successful. If making more money in the family business becomes meaningless and seems not to benefit anyone, the child is heading for trouble. Sigmund Freud told us that the principal sources of self-esteem and meaning in life are love *and work*. Work that fulfills is critically important to trillionheirs' welfare. Few of us can maintain our self-esteem without working. A trillionheir may be fulfilled in the arts or the humanities, or in teaching, government, politics, or even social work.

Numerous trillionheirs have found fulfillment in careers that don't generate much money such as the arts. Others have found fulfillment in charitable pursuits either as a career or as an avocation. Most trillionheirs like work environments in which they are not perceived as "different". Most are tempted to quit when, inevitably, the going gets rough. It may be hard for them to recognize the benefit of enduring pain when pain can be so easily avoided."

Women in my family don't worry about equal treatment. They won't get it.

My family needs a son who's a poet.

My family preaches that respectable careers for men make money. Period.

I'll start a Camp Denim commune for grownups.

We'll work at what fulfills us regardless of income.

The rich ones will sponsor one other that can't afford it.

We'll all wear denim and help with the chores.

Oh dear, isn't that what chased grandpa out of China?!

Relationships Are Crucial. "Trillionheirs need friends who are not resentful or envious and who are not out to exploit the relationship. Wealthy or not such friends need to relate to a wealthy friend without flattery or manipulation."

Self-confidence. "Trillionheirs least damaged by their fortunes are those who have proven to themselves that they don't need family money in order to lead successful lives. To generate this self-reliance they need some meaningful and successful experience at earning a living—a kind of "Outward Bound" experience. Self-confidence can only come from situations that require self-reliance."

Taking Risks With People. "Suspiciousness comes with the territory. But trillionheirs need to risk commitment to lovers, friends and associates. The risk of being hurt is always present. To trust another person is a primary requirement for maturity. There will be disappointments, disillusionments and pain. But the rewards are worth the risks. And risking is the only way we can know that a person can be trusted."

How can I be sure that someone doesn't care about my money . . . or isn't after my money . . . unless they're wealthy too?

How can I really risk trusting someone who isn't wealthy also?

Do being wealthy and being paranoid necessarily go together?

Do I need to make a fortune to prove I don't need the fortune I inherited?

Stewardship. "There is a striking correlation between a keen sense of social responsibility and comfort and satisfaction with being wealthy. Giving or investing for the benefit of society provides a sense of meaning and purpose. Wealthy European families (who handle wealth better than Americans) put great emphasis on the wealth's responsibilities."

We talked about "stewardship" around the table at Camp Denim without using the word.

The word comes from "sty ward", keeper of the pigs.

Avery is certainly a steward of her medical skills and Fred is learning.

In his way I suppose Ernesto is a steward of his opportunities.

Sallie is still hung up on how she got her wealth.

Perhaps one day Sallie will consider stewardship.

Roger is fascinated with wealth itself. I wish he were as curious about stewardship.

Connie is a steward of her voice—and the anonymous Benefactor of Camp Denim, as I happened to discover.

Does Skipper shine her red boots?

My family helps destitute Chinese families.

Do you really need to give lots away in order to be comfortable and satisfied with the wealth you keep?

Choosing a Lifestyle. "Trillionheirs should choose a lifestyle that fits them. If they crave a luxurious lifestyle let them test it out. If they wish to live modestly they can certainly afford it. Avoid a lifestyle dictated by their parents or by what others think of them. Be prepared for lifestyle preference to shift and change as you grow older. Lifestyle decisions are your own."

Wealthy parents can stake you to a lifestyle you can't otherwise afford as a way of controlling you. Bad scene.

Wealthy parents can stake you to a lifestyle that doesn't embarrass them! Bad scene.

So long as parents supply the money what's wrong with living in a style that pleases them? Is that like being a kid on an allowance?

Parents and peers can make you feel good about your lifestyle because it fits you.

The Bad News. "We have certainly seen low self-esteem, delayed maturity, lack of motivation and poor self-discipline.

"We have seen incredible boredom, improvident use of power and lots of guilt.

"We have seen undue suspicion of non-affluent persons, the sting of their envy and the inclination to stay with one's own wealthy kind for mutual emotional protection.

"We have seen persons paralyzed by unlimited options and the disabling fear of losing wealth.

"We have seen talented wealthy people crave notoriety for their personal accomplishments, unconnected to wealth.

"We have seen too much reliance on household workers as surrogate parents and unrealistic expectations of children who lack the talent."

That's really depressing!

The Good News. "We have seen the other side, too.

"We have seen parents and children drawn much closer together through full disclosures about the family fortune and the process of intergenerational estate planning.

"We know wealthy parents who understand there can be no parental substitute, who steadfastly refuse to hire someone to raise their children and who are wise enough to encourage healthy relationships with adult role models who aren't necessarily wealthy themselves.

"We know parents who understand they must teach stewardship of wealth by example, and they do.

"We know parents who are very candid about the origins of their wealth even if the history is not very presentable.

"We know parents who have successfully transmitted the zeal for doing business to their children—children who will succeed them gladly and successfully.

"We know wealthy children who have chosen fulfilling careers outside the business world.

"We know wealthy families who have and are teaching a high sense of stewardship over the family fortune and the position and privileges wealth affords them.

"We know trillionheirs who take the necessary risks to form deep and abiding human relationships."

Let's go for it!